HEALTHY CHOICES

EVERYDAY RECIPES
for
HEALTHY EATING

Published in cooperation with the

CANADIAN DIABETES ASSOCIATION | **ASSOCIATION CANADIENNE DU DIABÈTE**

Recipes selected by Sheila Walker
and edited by Beverley Renahan.

Canadian Cataloguing in Publication Data
Main entry under title:

Healthy choices

Includes index.
ISBN 0-7715-9163-2

1. Diabetes - Diet therapy - Recipes.
I. Canadian Diabetes Association.

RC662.H43 1992   641.5' 6314   C92-093193-6

Distributed in Canada by Macmillan Canada
(A Division of Canada Publishing Corporation)

Order via Gage Distribution
164 Commander Boulevard
Agincourt, Ontario, M1S 3C7
Order Desk: (416) 293-8141
Fax: (416) 293-0846

Produced by
Partners Publishing
66 Kennedy Avenue
Toronto, Ontario, Canada, M6S 2X7
Ph: (416) 760-8878

On our cover: Mexican Stir-Fry Salad (p.82)

Printed and bound in Canada

Bound to stay open

Otabind (Ota-bind). This book has been bound using the patented Otabind process. You can open this book at any page, gently run your finger down the spine, and the pages will lie flat.

TABLE
OF
CONTENTS

PUBLISHER'S ACKNOWLEDGEMENTS

The development of a high quality, healthy eating cookbook is a large undertaking. Combine this with the detailed nutrition and Food Choice Value analysis required for proper diabetes meal planning, and you require a very committed team of individuals specializing in both food nutrition and diabetes health care. Partners Publishing would like to thank those key individuals associated directly or indirectly with the Canadian Diabetes Association for all their time and effort in helping to prepare *Healthy Choices*:

- Janie Sanderson, for overseeing this project from start to finish, with a desire to make this book a highly useful and reliable tool for those with diabetes.
- Sheila Walker, for her careful review/selection of recipes and calculation of Food Choice Values.
- Fran Berkhoff, for her overview of recipes and overall layout.
- Kathy Younker-Smith, for her detail orientation, humour, and quick turnarounds.
- Gillian Seaman, for being available to discuss a variety of diabetes related issues.

We would also like to thank those involved in the general publication of the book; including Bev Renahan for her excellent review and editing of the recipes, Bob Dees and Denise Schon, plus our production staff who gave up so many weekends and evenings. Also, a special personal thanks to Janet McLennan for her support.

Nutrition analysis was provided by Info Access and Brownridge Communications.

A very special thanks to Canada's Food Marketing Agencies, for their support and allowing us to select and utilize some of their very best and nutritious recipes and photographs:

Dairy Bureau of Canada   Canadian Egg Marketing Agency
Beef Information Centre   Canadian Chicken Marketing Agency
Canadian Turkey Marketing Agency   Canada Pork
Foodland Ontario

We also wish to thank corporate supporters: Lifescan Canada, Becton Dickinson & Eli Lilly.
(This does not contstitute an endorsement by the Canadian Diabetes Association.)

FOREWORD

From the Canadian Diabetes Association:

Eating is an important part of everyone's life. For the person with diabetes, meals have special meaning because they are a significant part of healthy living. This cookbook, with recipes from appetizers to desserts, will add zest and variety to meals, not only for people who have diabetes, but also for anyone who enjoys flavorful food. The Canadian Diabetes Association has assigned Food Choice Values to each recipe to help you achieve portion control with your Meal Plan.

For those who like international cuisine, this cookbook offers Greek, Italian, Mexican and Chinese recipes. If you enjoy a fast-paced lifestyle, you'll appreciate the microwave instructions and the Quick Meals section.

Nutritious meal planning does take some thought, especially when diabetes is involved. *Healthy Choices* will provide the information you need to create delicious meals to share with friends and family, both everyday and on special occasions.

Enjoy your *Healthy Choices!*

Janie Sanderson, M.Sc., R.P.Dt.
Manager of Nutrition Education &
Services, Canadian Diabetes Association.

The Canadian Diabetes Association is a non-profit association with offices in every province. Check your telephone directory for the office nearest you. They can provide programs and educational materials for those interested in obtaining information on diabetes.

INTRODUCTION

Most people, including those with diabetes, want to eat a nutritious variety of foods from all food groups. Many cookbooks have recipes that are high in sugar and fat, and do not include nutrient analysis about the carbohydrate, protein and fat content of each serving. This information is vital to people with diabetes using the Food Choice System. *Healthy Choices* contains nearly 200 carefully selected, kitchen tested recipes from Canada's Food Marketing Agencies. Each recipe has been reviewed for its suitability to diabetes meal planning by a team of nutritionists specializing in diabetes. Food Choice Value information per serving is included with each recipe, using the Food Choice Symbols familiar to Canadians who have diabetes.

These healthy and great-tasting recipes reflect the changing lifestyles of many Canadians. Microwave, Quick and Mini Meal recipes are included for working chefs on the run and younger family members learning to cook. (Over 50 appetizing color photographs encourage even the most reluctant kitchen explorer.) Popular and fun ethnic favorites, such as Asian and Mexican foods, are also included. The large Main Meals section is organized by favorite food type (Beef, Chicken, etc.), which is handy for last-minute meal planning or for using leftovers. Nutrient values are calculated for single servings of each recipe using current Food Composition tables. These figures are approximate due to the variations between tables and the many factors which can alter the yield of a recipe.

Healthy Choices is different from other cookbooks because it is user friendly, particularly to those with diabetes. The title page of each section is both an index and a summary of each recipe's Food Choice Values, and whether the recipe is Microwaveable. Nutritional symbols on recipes indicate whether the recipe is High In Fibre (4+ grams/serving) and Good* or Excellent* sources of Calcium & Iron. Descriptive symbols indicate whether a meal can be Prepared Ahead, is Spicy or a Kids Favorite. All recipes are measured in both Metric and Imperial, so you can pick the system you prefer. (Slight variations occur between metric and imperial systems, so it is important not to switch systems in the middle of a recipe. Pick one system and stay with it.)

For people with diabetes, following a meal plan is important. In the past this often meant giving up favorite foods. Using this book, everyday healthy eating has never been easier or tastier.

Good indicates that each serving provides 15% of an average persons recommended daily intake.
  Excellent indicates that each serving provides 25% of an average persons recommended daily intake.

TIPS FOR USING THIS BOOK

If you have Diabetes, here are some important tips on how to use this book:

1. You may be surprised to see that a few of the recipes in this book contain sugar. The Food Choice Values on the recipes have been calculated including the sugar, so there is no need to replace it with a sugar substitute. Be sure to use the serving size stated in the Food Choice Value when fitting it into your Meal Plan.

2. You will also note that some of the recipes contain various types of **alcohol** If the recipe calls for only a few tablespoons of alcohol, and the food is cooked for some time (as instructed on the recipe), it is likely that the alcohol will have evaporated leaving only the desirable flavor. If however, there is more than a few tablespoons of alcohol in the recipe., it may not all evaporate in the suggested cooking time. In this case, please note the recipe side column comment: "Ask your dietitian or doctor about the use of alcohol."

3. Many of the recipes in this book call for Milk, Cottage Cheese or Yogurt. Unless otherwise stated in the recipe listing, Food Choice Values have been calculated as follows:

   - Milk (2% fat)   • Cottage Cheese (2% fat)   • Yogurt, plain low-fat (1.5% fat)

4. In some recipes, some of the ingredients are listed as being optional. For example, on page 79, "Grated Parmesan Cheese (optional)". Please note that the Food Choice Values on the recipe do not include any optional foods. If you are unsure whether these optional foods will significantly alter the Food Choice Value for your serving, please ask your dietitian.

5. Some recipes, especially those in the Main Meals section, tell you to cook the food on a greased grill. Please note that the fat needed to grease the grill has not been included in the Food Choice Value. We recommend that you use a pan with a non-stick coating, lightly sprayed with "no-stick" cooking spray. This will not significantly alter the Food Choice Value. If you are using a regular pan, use the same "no-stick" cooking spray OR use additional fat from your diabetes Meal Plan.

6. If your dietitian has taught you how to assign Food Choice Values, you may wonder why the grams of carbohydrate in the Food Choice Values on some recipes, seem lower than the grams of carbohydrate stated in the recipe. This is because the grams of fibre (in the recipe), were first subtracted from the total carbohydrate in the recipe. The Food Choice Value was then assigned to the remaining grams of carbohydrate. For example, this occurs on the recipe for Chicken Minestrone soup on page 56.

CANADIAN DIABETES ASSOCIATION'S FOOD GROUP SYSTEM

People with diabetes need to balance their food intake with their insulin supply. This balance can be achieved by following a Meal Plan which has been tailored to the individual with the help of a qualified dietitian. Factors such as lifestyle, activity level, weight goals, food allergies and food preferences are very important in the design of the Meal Plan. In Canada, a Food Group system is used to make meal planning simpler. Foods are sorted into one of six groups according to their carbohydrate, fat and protein content. Each group is identified by a symbol for easy recognition. The word "Choice" refers to a measured or weighed amount of food in each group. Choices within a group are interchangeable because they are considered to have similar carbohydrate, fat or protein content. Choices from one group cannot be exchanged for Choices from another group. Each list below shows how much to eat for 1 Choice from the specified Food Groups.

FOOD GROUPS

STARCHY FOODS GROUP ▢

Starchy foods include breads, cereals, grains, pasta, dried beans/peas, starchy vegetables, and some prepared foods. These foods contain complex forms of carbohydrate which break down to sugar during digestion.

Some starchy foods are valuable sources of dietary fibre. Fibre helps to slow down the rate at which sugar enters the blood stream. High fibre foods may also help to promote weight loss as they help to create a feeling of fullness which results in eating less food. To increase your fibre intake, eat a variety of foods such as dried beans, peas, lentils, whole grain breads and cereals.

If you enjoy eating out, here are some helpful Starchy Food Choices values: 1 scoop of rice, potato or stuffing is about 125 mL (1/2 cup) and equals 1 Starchy Foods Choice. Remember, these items may contain extra fat which give extra Calories.

1 Choice († = Measure after cooking)

bread	1 slice	muffin, plain	1 small
cereal*, hot† or cold	125 mL (1/2 cup)	noodles†	125 mL (1/2 cup)
crackers	8 small	plain cookies*	2
corn on the cob	1/2 medium	potato (small)	1/2
corn, kernel	125 mL (1/2 cup)	potato, whipped†	125mL (1/2 cup)
dinner roll	1 small	rice, other grains†	125 mL (1/2 cup)
dried peas/beans†	125mL (1/2 cup)	shredded wheat	1 round
hamburger bun	1/2	soup*	250 mL (1 cup)
macaroni†	125 mL (1/2 cup)	spaghetti†	125 mL (1/2 cup)
melba toast	4 slices		

*For more specific measures of cereals, cookies and soups, see *Food Choices in the Marketplace* published by the Canadian Diabetes Association.

FRUITS & VEGETABLES GROUP

This group includes fruits and many vegetables. Since certain vegetables, such as corn and potatoes are high in starch, they are included in the Starchy Foods Group. Fruits and vegetables are excellent sources of many vitamins and minerals as well as dietary fibre. For help in using Fruits & Vegetables Choices, follow these tips:

1. Buy fruits and juices which have been canned or frozen without sugar.

2. Eat fruits and vegetables rather than drinking juices. The natural sugar present in juice enters the blood rapidly, while the fibre content of solid fruits and vegetables helps to slow the rise in blood sugar.

3. Serve and eat fruits such as apples or pears by the slice. Your portion, cut into a number of slices, will seem like more.

<u>1 Choice</u> (Fresh, water-packed, canned or frozen; no sugar added.)

apple	1/2 medium	plums	2
applesauce	125 mL (1/2 cup)	pineapple	125 mL (1/2 cup)
apricots	2	prunes	2
banana	1/2 small	raisins	30 mL (2 tbsp)
berries	125 mL (1/2 cup)	strawberries	250 mL (1 cup)
canteloupe	1/4	watermelon	250 mL (1 cup)
cherries	125 mL (1/2 cup)	beets	125 mL (1/2 cup)
dates	2	carrots	125 mL (1/2 cup)
grapefruit	1/2	mixed vegetables	125 mL (1/2 cup)
grapes	125 mL (1/2 cup)	peas	125 mL (1/2 cup)
orange	1 small	squash	125 mL (1/2 cup)
peach	1	tomatoes, canned	250 mL (1 cup)
pear	1/2	turnip	125 mL (1/2 cup)

Unsweetened Juices

tomato, vegetable	250 mL (1 cup)	apple, pineapple	75mL (1/3 cup)
grapefruit, orange	125 mL (1/2 cup)	grape, prune	50mL (1/4 cup)

MILK GROUP ◆

This group includes milk and yogurt. Your dietitian will tell you the type of milk you should use in your Meal Plan. For help in using Milk Choices, follow these tips:

1. Measure your milk; do not guess.

2. Mix cream soups with water unless you use milk from your milk allowance.

3. Plain yogurt may be substituted for milk, but avoid sweetened yogurts which have a "fruit bottom" or added syrup. They usually contain extra sugar.

<u>1 Choice</u>

milk, fluid	125 mL (1/2 cup)
milk, powdered	30 mL (2 tbsp)
milk, canned, evaporated	50 mL (1/4 cup)
cheese	small wedge + 3 crackers
plain yogurt	125 mL (1/2 cup)

PROTEIN FOODS GROUP ▨

This group includes meat, fish, poultry, cheese and eggs. When shopping, buy enough meat to allow for shrinkage during cooking; 100g (4 oz) raw, boneless meat will yield about 75g (3 oz) cooked. When selecting chops or poultry, purchase double the weight required; 500g (1 lb) raw poultry or chops will yield about 250g (1/2 lb) cooked. All weights and measures are for cooked meats, fish and poultry unless otherwise stated. For help in using Protein Choices follow these tips:

1. When shopping for meat, select cuts which look lean and have little visible fat distributed (marbled) throughout. Remember that wieners, sausages, luncheon meats and cheeses may contain extra (hidden) fat, so use them less often.

2. Use cooking methods which help remove fat, such as baking, barbecuing, broiling, roasting, stewing and boiling. Fry meats in a non-stick pan lightly sprayed with a "no-stick" cooking spray.

3. Drain or trim excess fat from protein foods before eating them or combining them with other foods.

4. Remove fat from pan juices of cooked meats and use the fat-free juice instead of gravy.

1 Choice († = Measure after cooking)

cheese (eg.cheddar,brick)	1 piece 5 cm x 2 cm x 2 cm (2" x 3/4" x 3/4")
cheese, packaged slices	1 slice
cottage cheese	50 mL (1/4 cup)
egg	1 medium
fish, canned, drained	50 mL (1/4 cup)
fish, fillet†	1 piece 6 cm x 2 cm x 2 cm (2 1/2" x 3/4" x 3/4")

Meat and poultry: (back bacon, beef, chicken, ham, lamb, pork, turkey, veal)

sliced †	1 piece 10 cm x 5 cm x 5 mm (4" x 2" x 1/4")
diced†	2 cubes each 25 mm square (1" square)
minced or ground†	30 mL (2 tbsp)
packaged slices	1 slice
chop, with bone†	1 small or 1/2 medium
steak†	1 piece 5 cm x 5 cm x 1 cm (2" x 2" x 1/2")
peanut butter	15 mL (1 tbsp)
scallops, clams, oysters	3 medium
shrimps	10 medium
wiener	1/2

FATS & OILS GROUP ◭

This group includes a variety of high fat foods such as vegetable oils, salad dressings, nuts, margarine and butter. All fats are very high in Calories. Be especially careful to measure fats and oils if weight loss is necessary. If you have been advised to use polyunsaturated fats, choose oils such as safflower, sunflower, corn and soyabean. For help in using Fats & Oils Choices, follow these tips:

1. Be especially careful to measure fats and oils. Count salad dressing, and also the oil, margarine or butter you use to cook or flavor your food.

2. Use broth, water, or vegetable juices instead of fats and oils when cooking.

1 Choice

bacon, side	1 strip	salad dressing,	10 mL (2 tsp)
butter	5 mL (1 tsp)	**Nuts & Seeds, shelled:**	
margarine	5 mL (1 tsp)	almonds	8
mayonnaise	5 mL (1 tsp)	cashews	5
oil	5 mL (1 tsp)	peanuts	10
shortening	5 mL (1 tsp)	walnut halves	4
cream, 10%	30 mL (2 tbsp)	sunflower seeds	15mL (1 tbsp)

EXTRA VEGETABLES ++

The vegetables in this group are low in natural sugar and energy, and they are high in dietary fibre, vitamins and minerals. Use them when you feel like nibbling. Moderate amounts of these vegetables do not have to be measured or calculated in your Meal Plan. Usually, 125 mL (1/2 cup) of cooked vegetables from this group contains less than 3.5 g of carbohydrate and yields an energy value of 60 kilojoules (14 Calories) or less. For some vegetables, 250 mL (1 cup) would be counted as one Fruits & Vegetables Choice ◪. These are indicated with an asterisk (*) in the following list.

asparagus	celery	peppers, red or green
beans, yellow or green	cucumber	radishes
bean sprouts	greens	rhubarb*
broccoli	lettuce	spinach
brussels sprouts*	mushrooms	tomato (2 medium)
cabbage	onions, cooking type*	vegetable marrow
cauliflower	parsley	zucchini

EXTRAS ++

The following foods can be used without measuring:

clear broth, consomé
clear coffee or tea
gelatin, unflavored
lemon juice or wedge
seasoning herbs, mustard, spices
jelly dessert, artificially sweetened.

salt, pepper
soda water/mineral water
sugar-free soft drinks
vinegar
water

The following foods can be used in small amounts, as indicated:

bran, natural	15 mL (1 tbsp)	ketchup	5 mL (1 tsp)
cocoa powder	5 mL (1 tsp)	sour pickle	1 medium
coffee whitener	5 mL (1 tsp)	sweet relish	5 mL (1 tsp)
diet spread	5 mL (1 tsp)	whipped topping	15 mL (1 tbsp)

FOODS TO AVOID X

chocolates
candies
condensed milk
honey
iced cakes, pastries
jams, jellies

molasses
regular soft drinks
syrup
sugar
sundae with syrup
tonic water

Note: Additional information is available in the *Good Health Eating Guide* booklet
published by the Canadian Diabetes Association addresses.

CANADIAN DIABETES ASSOCIATION | ASSOCIATION CANADIENNE DU DIABÈTE

For further information about diabetes, write to the Canadian Diabetes Association Divisional Office nearest you. There are 10 divisional offices, with 170 branches across Canada.

BRITISH COLUMBIA/ YUKON
1091 West 8th Avenue
Vancouver, British Columbia
V6H 2V3 (604) 732-1331

QUEBEC
180 boulevard René-Léveque est
bureau 200
Montréal, Quebec
H2X 1N6 (514) 398-0954

ALBERTA/ N.W.T.
#305, 10240-124th Street
Edmonton, Alberta
T5N 3W6 (403) 482-2307

NEW BRUNSWICK/ NOUVEAU BRUNSWICK
259 Brunswick, Suite 105
Fredericton, N. B.
E3B 1G8 (506) 452-9009

SASKATCHEWAN
2301 Avenue C.N., Suite 104
Saskatoon, Saskatchewan
S7L 5Z5 (306) 933-1238

NOVA SCOTIA
1221 Barrington Street
Halifax, Nova Scotia
B3J 1Y2 (902) 421-1444

MANITOBA
283 Portage Avenue
Winnipeg, Manitoba
R3B 2B5 (204) 943-7529

PRINCE EDWARD ISLAND
Box 133
Charlottetown, P.E.I.
C1A 7K2 (902) 894-3005

ONTARIO
747 Baseline Road East
London, Ontario
N6C 2R6 (519) 668-2782

NEWFOUNDLAND
Box 9130
St. John's Newfoundland
A1A 2X3 (709) 754-0953

Canadian Diabetes Association National Office:
78 Bond Street, Toronto, Ontario, M5B 2J8 *(416) 362-4440*

METRIC MEASURES

When measuring ingredients in a recipe, choose either Metric or Imperial measures throughout the whole recipe. Don't switch back and forth. Note that Metric and Imperial measures are somtimes rounded for ease of measuring, as follows:
15 mL = 1 tbsp, but 25 mL is measured as 2 tbsp.
3 tsp = 1tbsp = 45mL ; 4 tbsp = 1/4 cup = 50 mL.

Metric Replacements

Volume Measures

1 mL	=	1/4 tsp
2 mL	=	1/2 tsp
5 mL	=	1 tsp
10 mL	=	2 tsp
15 mL	=	1 tbsp (3 tsp)
25 mL	=	2 tbsp
45 mL	=	3 tbsp
50 mL	=	1/4 cup
75 mL	=	1/3 cup
125 mL	=	1/2 cup
250 mL	=	1 cup

Cake Pans/Dishes

2 L	=	8 inch square
2.5 L	=	9 inch square
3 L	=	12 x 8 inch rectangle
3.5 L	=	12 1/2 x 8 1/2 inch
4 L	=	13 x 9 inch rectangle
5 L	=	14 x 10 inch rectangle

Pie Plate/pan:

1 L	=	9 x 1 1/4 inch

Casserole Dish:

1 L	=	1 qt.

Loaf pan/dish:

1.5 L	=	8 x 4 x 3 inch
2L	=	9 x 5 x 3 inch
3 L	=	10 x 5 x 4 inch

NOTES

_____

_____

_____

_____

_____

_____

_____

_____

_____

BREADS
&
MUFFINS

	Microwave	Protein	Starchy	Fruits & Vegetables	Fats & Oils	Page
Savory Cheddar Bread *(Photo: p. 17)*		1/2	1 1/2		1	19
Blueberry Almond Loaf *(Photo: p. 17)*			1	1	1	20
Herb Scones with Onions *(Photo: p. 17)*			2		2	21
Tropical Fruit Muffins			1	1	1 1/2	22
Easy Oven Pancake Squares		1/2	1 1/2	1	1	23
Cheddar Nugget Bread			1 1/2		1	24
Peanut Butter Muffins			1	1	1 1/2	25
Surprise Peach Muffins			1		2	26
Dutch Apple Pancake		1	1	1/2	1 1/2	27
Pineapple Muffins			1		1/2	28

The Food Choice Values on each recipe do not include accompanying foods which are suggested in many of the recipes and shown in some of the photographs.

Savory Cheddar Bread (p.19)

Blueberry Almond Loaf (p.20)

Herb Scones with Onions (p.21)

17

Turkey Nuggets With Curry Dip (p.30)

Tomato Pan Bagna (p.33)

Icy Yogurt Pops (p.32)

Savory Cheddar Bread

PHOTO ON PAGE 17.

There's nothing more heart-warming and comforting than the tantalizing aroma of freshly baked bread wafting through the house. This appetizing recipe adds zest to an everyday staple. Textured and flavorful, this makes a wonderful after-school snack, but also doubles as a great appetizer for guests.

500 mL	all-purpose flour	2 cups
20 mL	baking powder	4 tsp
15 mL	granulated sugar	1 tbsp
2 mL	onion salt	1/2 tsp
2 mL	crushed dried oregano	1/2 tsp
1 mL	dry mustard	1/4 tsp
300 mL	shredded Cheddar cheese	1 1/4 cups
1	egg, well beaten	1
250 mL	milk	1 cup
15 mL	butter, melted	1 tbsp

In bowl, stir together flour, baking powder, sugar, onion salt, oregano, mustard and cheese.

Combine egg, milk and butter; add all at once to dry ingredients, stirring just until moistened.

Spread batter in greased 1.5 L (4-1/2 x 8-1/2-inch) loaf pan. Bake in 180°C (350°F) oven 45 minutes. Cool 10 minutes on rack. Remove from pan. Slice to serve.

Makes 1 loaf.

FOOD CHOICE VALUE *per serving*

Each Serving: 1/12 loaf (56g/2.0 oz)

1/2	☑ *Protein Choice*
1 1/2	☐ *Starchy Choices*
1	▲ *Fats & Oils Choice*

19 g	Carbohydrate
6 g	Protein
6 g	Total Fat
664	kilojoules *(158 Calories)*

Blueberry Almond Loaf

Toasted almonds add texture to this flavorful loaf. Cut into thin strips for between-meal treats. Serve it to friends on weekend afternoons, its especially good with tea.

PHOTO ON PAGE 17.

1	*egg*	*1*
375 mL	*milk*	*1 1/2 cups*
50 mL	*butter or soft margarine, melted*	*1/4 cup*
375 mL	*100% Bran cereal*	*1 1/2 cups*
375 mL	*all-purpose flour*	*1 1/2 cups*
125 mL	*granulated sugar*	*1/2 cup*
15 mL	*baking powder*	*1 tbsp*
2 mL	*cinnamon*	*1/2 tsp*
2 mL	*salt*	*1/2 tsp*
125 mL	*sliced almonds, toasted*	*1/2 cup*
250 mL	*blueberries, fresh or frozen (unthawed)*	*1 cup*

To toast almonds, spread on baking sheet and bake in 180°C (350°F) oven for 3 to 5 minutes until lightly browned.

Beat together egg, milk and butter; stir in cereal and let stand to soften.

In large bowl, mix together flour, sweetener, baking powder, cinnamon and salt; stir in almonds. Stir in cereal mixture just until moistened. Fold in blueberries.

Spread evenly in greased 2 L (9 x 5-inch) loaf pan. Bake in 180°C (350°F) oven for 60 to 70 minutes or until tester inserted in centre comes out clean. Cool in pan 10 minutes, then turn out onto rack to cool completely. Store in airtight container. Slice and serve.

Makes 1 loaf (14 slices), each slice 70g/2.5 oz.

FOOD CHOICE VALUE *per serving*

Each Serving: 1 slice

1	☐	*Starchy Choice*
1	◪	*Fruits & Vegetables Choice*
1	▲	*Fats & Oils Choice*

26 g	*Carbohydrate*
4 g	*Protein*
6 g	*Total Fat*
710	*kilojoules (169 Calories)*

Herb Scones Topped with Onions

PHOTO ON PAGE 17.

Full of goodness and spiced with a delicate blend of herbs, these savory scones are a guaranteed taste sensation. For added variety, replace the onion topping with grated cheese. These make a lovely treat for Sunday brunch.

25 mL	*butter or soft margarine*	*2 tbsp*
2	*medium onions, halved lengthwise and sliced*	*2*
1 mL	*dried thyme*	*1/4 tsp*
1	*egg*	*1*
175 mL	*milk*	*3/4 cup*
250 mL	*100% Bran cereal*	*1 cup*
425 mL	*all-purpose flour*	*1 3/4 cups*
15 mL	*baking powder*	*1 tbsp*
2 mL	*salt*	*1/2 tsp*
2 mL	*dried basil*	*1/2 tsp*
2 mL	*dried oregano*	*1/2 tsp*
50 mL	*butter or soft margarine*	*1/4 cup*

In skillet over medium heat, melt butter; sauté onions about 5 minutes or until tender. Stir in thyme and cook 1 minute longer. Set aside.

Beat together egg and milk; stir in cereal to soften. Mix flour, baking powder, salt, basil and oregano; cut in butter with 2 knives or food processor until crumbly. Stir into cereal mixture, stirring just until moistened.

Turn out onto floured board; knead gently 10 times. Roll with floured rolling pin to 20 cm (8-inch) circle. Place on baking sheet.

Score surface into 8 wedges. Spread onion mixture evenly on top. Bake in 220°C (425°F) oven for 20 to 35 minutes or until browned. Cool on rack. Cut into wedges and serve warm.

Makes 8 scones, each 85g/3 oz.

FOOD CHOICE VALUE *per serving*

Each Serving: 1 scone

2	☐	*Starchy Choices*
2	▲	*Fats & Oils Choices*

30 g	*Carbohydrate*
6 g	*Protein*
10 g	*Total Fat*
941	*kilojoules (224 Calories)*

Tropical Fruit Muffins

Sunny flavors in fresh-from-the-oven muffins will brighten up any dreary day. Excellent for breakfast or anytime snacks.

500 mL	*all-purpose flour*	*2 cups*
10 mL	*baking powder*	*2 tsp*
5 mL	*baking soda*	*1 tsp*
2	*eggs*	*2*
250 mL	*mashed ripe bananas*	*1 cup*
175 mL	*no-sugar-added apricot spread*	*3/4 cup*
125 mL	*unsweetened pineapple juice*	*1/2 cup*
75 mL	*vegetable oil*	*1/3 cup*
50 mL	*finely chopped walnuts*	*1/4 cup*

In large bowl, stir together flour, baking powder and baking soda; set aside.

In medium bowl, beat eggs. Add bananas, apricot spread, pineapple juice and oil; beat until well combined. Add to dry ingredients all at once; stir just until moistened. Stir in nuts.

Divide batter evenly among 12 greased medium muffin cups. Bake in 190°C (375°F) oven 20 to 25 minutes or until tops are firm to the touch.

Makes one dozen medium muffins.

Instead of greasing the muffin cups, you can use paper liners.

FOOD CHOICE VALUE	*per serving*
Each Serving: 1 muffin	
1	☐ *Starchy Choice*
1	◩ *Fruits & Vegetables Choice*
1 1/2	◩ *Fats & Oils Choices*
26 g	*Carbohydrate*
4 g	*Protein*
8 g	*Total Fat*
802	*kilojoules (191 Calories)*

Easy Oven Pancake Squares

Everyone's favorite breakfast treat is made simpler and quicker with this easy-to-bake recipe. Just pop this into the oven while the coffee is brewing. Instead of topping with maple syrup, try fresh fruit or fruit mixed with yogurt.

300 mL	all-purpose flour	1 1/4 cups
12 mL	baking powder	2 1/2 tsp
4 mL	salt	3/4 tsp
1	egg	1
300 mL	skim milk	1 1/4 cups
25 mL	no-sugar-added table syrup	2 tbsp
15 mL	butter or soft margarine, melted	1 tbsp
	GARNISH	
135 mL	no-sugar-added table syrup	9 tbsp
50 mL	chopped walnuts, toasted	3 tbsp

In medium bowl, stir together flour, baking powder and salt.
In small bowl, beat egg; stir in milk, 25 mL (2 tbsp) table syrup and butter. Add to dry ingredients, beating until smooth.

Pour batter into greased 3.5 L (13 x 9-inch) baking dish.
Bake in 220°C (425°F) oven 10 to 12 minutes or until done.

Cut into 12 squares. Pour table syrup over each serving.
Garnish with walnuts.

Makes 6 servings.

FOOD CHOICE VALUE *per serving*

Each Serving: 1/6 of recipe

1/2	☑	*Protein Choice*
1 1/2	☐	*Starchy Choices*
1	◣	*Fruits & Vegetables Choice*
1	▲	*Fats & Oils Choice*

30 g	*Carbohydrate*
6 g	*Protein*
6 g	*Total Fat*
819	*kilojoules (195 Calories)*

Cheddar Nugget Bread

Canada is famous for its tangy Cheddar cheese – so try it with this homemade treat. Slice it warm from the oven – it borders on the sensational.

25 mL	*sugar, divided*	*2 tbsp*
125 mL	*warm water*	*1/2 cup*
1	*pkg active dry yeast*	*1*
250 mL	*milk*	*1 cup*
25 mL	*butter/melted*	*2 tbsp*
7 mL	*salt*	*1 1/2 tsp*
1 L	*all-purpose flour*	*4 cups*
375 mL	*shredded old Cheddar cheese*	*1 1/2 cups*

In large bowl, dissolve 10 mL (2 tsp) of the sugar in warm water. Stir in yeast; let stand 10 minutes. Add milk, butter, remaining sugar and salt. Stir in about 750 mL (3 cups) flour to make stiff dough.

Turn out onto floured board. Knead until elastic, working in additional flour, about 8 minutes. Place in greased bowl, turning to grease all over. Cover; let rise in warm place until doubled in bulk, about 1 hour.

Punch dough down. Turn out onto lightly floured board. Roll out into 30 x 35 cm (12 x 14-inch) rectangle. Sprinkle with cheese. Roll up jelly roll-style, starting at long side; cut roll into 2.5 cm (1-inch) sections. Cut each section into quarters.

Divide evenly between two foil-lined 1.5 L (8-1/2 x 4-1/2-inch) loaf pans. (Do not let cut surfaces of dough touch sides or bottoms of pans.) Cover; let rise in warm place until doubled in bulk, about 1 hour. Bake in 180°C (350°F) oven 25 to 30 minutes or until loaves sound hollow when tapped. Remove from pans; cool on racks.

Makes 2 loaves.

FOOD CHOICE VALUE *per serving*

Each Serving: 1/12 loaf (42g/1.5 oz)

1 1/2 ☐ *Starchy Choices*

1 ▲ *Fats & Oils Choice*

20 g	*Carbohydrate*
5 g	*Protein*
4 g	*Total Fat*
563	*kilojoules (134 Calories)*

Peanut Butter Muffins with Banana Chunks

These muffins are reminiscent of the favorite sandwich – only better!
Great for packed lunches or after school snacks.

1	*egg*	*1*
375 mL	*milk*	*1-1/2 cups*
125 mL	*crunchy peanut butter*	*1/2 cup*
125 mL	*brown sugar*	*1/2 cup*
50 mL	*vegetable oil*	*1/4 cup*
250 mL	*100% Bran cereal*	*1 cup*
2	*medium bananas*	*2*
500 mL	*all-purpose flour*	*2 cups*
15 mL	*baking powder*	*1 tbsp*
1 mL	*salt*	*1/4 tsp*

Grease 18 medium sized muffin tins or line with paper baking cups.

Beat together egg, milk, peanut butter, sweetener and oil until
well combined. Stir in cereal, let stand 5 minutes.

Slice bananas lengthwise in quarters and cut crosswise into chunks;
stir into cereal mixture.

In large bowl, combine flour, baking powder and salt; stir in cereal
mixture just until moistened.

Spoon into muffin cups, evenly filling each cup. Bake in 200°C
(400°F) oven for about 20 minutes or until tops are firm to the
touch.. Cool on rack. Store in airtight container.

Makes 18 medium muffins, each 65 g (2 1/2 oz).

FOOD CHOICE VALUE *per serving*

Each Serving : 1 Muffin

1	☐	*Starchy Choice*
1	◪	*Fruits&Vegetables Choice*
1 1/2	◣	*Fats & Oils Choices*

24 g	*Carbohydrate*
5 g	*Protein*
8 g	*Total Fat*
692	*kilojoules (173 Calories)*

Surprise Peach Muffins

Enjoy these piping hot muffins, oozing with a low-calorie filling that doubles as a breakfast spread for toast or muffins.

250 mL	*all-purpose flour*	*1 cup*
22 mL	*baking powder*	*1 1/2 tbsp*
2 mL	*cinnamon*	*1/2 tsp*
2 mL	*nutmeg*	*1/2 tsp*
175 mL	*sliced peeled fresh peaches*	*3/4 cup*
125 mL	*skim milk*	*1/2 cup*
1	*egg*	*1*
50 mL	*margarine, melted*	*1/4 cup*

GLAZE

Sugar substitute equivalent to 25 mL (2 tbsp) sugar

25 mL	*water*	*2 tbsp*

FILLING

75 mL	*soft margarine*	*1/3 cup*

Sugar substitute equivalent to 40 mL (8 tsp) sugar

2 mL	*vanilla*	*1/2 tsp*

In bowl, mix together flour, baking powder, cinnamon and nutmeg. In food processor or blender, purée peaches; blend in milk, egg and margarine until smooth. Add to flour mixture; mix just until moistened.

Pour evenly into 8 muffin tins sprayed with nonstick vegetable spray. Bake in 200°C (400°F) oven 15 to 20 minutes or until tops are firm to the touch. Remove from oven; prick tops with fork.

Glaze: Blend sweetener with water; brush on top of each muffin.

Filling: Mix margarine, sweetener and vanilla; pipe into centre of each muffin from bottom or serve with muffins as spread.

Makes 8 muffins.

FOOD CHOICE VALUE *per serving*

Each Serving:

1	☐	*Starchy Choice*
2	◣	*Fats & Oils Choices*

17 g	*Carbohydrate*
3 g	*Protein*
9 g	*Total Fat*
693	*kilojoules (166 Calories)*

Dutch Apple Pancake

For a cheery start to the day, serve this pancake accompanied with a low sugar strawberry breakfast spread or top with fresh fruit.

4	eggs	4
125 mL	all-purpose flour	1/2 cup
2 mL	baking powder	1/2 tsp
0.5 mL	salt	1/8 tsp
125 mL	skim milk	1/2 cup
5 mL	vanilla	1 tsp
25 mL	soft margarine, melted	2 tbsp
0.5 mL	cinnamon	1/8 tsp

FILLING

25 mL	soft margarine	2 tbsp
1	large tart apple, peeled and sliced 5 mm (1/4 inch) thick	1
2 mL	cinnamon	1/2 tsp

GLAZE

Sugar substitute equivalent to 75 mL (1/3 cup) sugar

2 mL	cinnamon	1/2 tsp
50 mL	boiling water	3 tbsp

In blender or food processor, combine eggs, flour, baking powder, salt, milk, vanilla, margarine and cinnamon; process until smooth.

Filling: In 25 cm (10-inch) ovenproof skillet, melt margarine over low heat. Add apple and cinnamon; cook, stirring often, for 3 minutes. Pour batter over apples; bake in 220°C (425°F) oven for 15 minutes. Reduce heat to 180°C (350°F); bake for 15 minutes.

Glaze: Blend together sweetener, cinnamon and boiling water; drizzle over pancake. Cut into wedges to serve.

Makes 4 servings.

FOOD CHOICE VALUE *per serving*

Each Serving: 1/4 of recipe

1	⊘ Protein Choice
1	☐ Starchy Choice
1/2	◨ Fruits & Vegetables Choice
1 1/2	▲ Fats & Oils Choices

22 g	Carbohydrate
9 g	Protein
10 g	Total Fat
937	kilojoules (223 Calories)

Pineapple Muffins

All the goodness of the South Seas bursts from these muffins with their pineapple centers. These muffins are moist enough to not need butter. Be sure to keep plenty of muffins in the freezer for when guests drop by.

375 mL	*all-purpose flour*	*1 1/2 cups*
10 mL	*baking powder*	*2 tsp*
2 mL	*salt*	*1/2 tsp*
2 mL	*cinnamon*	*1/2 tsp*
1 mL	*nutmeg*	*1/4 tsp*
125 mL	*skim milk*	*1/2 cup*
2	*eggs (or 3 egg whites)*	*2*
25 mL	*vegetable oil*	*2 tbsp*
1	*can (213 g / 8 oz) unsweetened, crushed pineapple, drained*	*1*

GLAZE
Sugar substitute equivalent to 75 mL (1/3 cup) sugar

1 mL	*cinnamon*	*1/4 tsp*
50 mL	*boiling water*	*3 tbsp*

In bowl, combine flour, baking powder, salt, cinnamon and nutmeg; mix in milk, eggs, oil and pineapple, stirring just until moistened.

Spoon into 12 muffin cups sprayed with nonstick vegetable spray. Bake in 200°C (400°F) oven about 22 minutes or until golden brown. Remove from oven; prick tops in centre with fork.

Glaze: Blend together sweetener, cinnamon and boiling water; drizzle evenly over muffins. Remove to rack. Serve warm.

Makes 12 muffins, each 100g/3 1/2 oz.

Muffins may be cooled completely, wrapped individually and frozen up to 3 months. To reheat in microwave, wrap each muffin in a paper towel and microwave at HIGH (100% power) 45 to 50 seconds, turning after 30 seconds of cooking.

FOOD CHOICE VALUE *per serving*

Each Serving: 1 muffin

1	☐	*Starchy Choice*
1/2	◣	*Fats & Oils Choice*

17 g	*Carbohydrate*
3 g	*Protein*
3 g	*Total Fat*
449	*kilojoules (107 Calories)*

LUNCHES & SNACKS

	Microwave	Protein	Starchy	Milk	Fruits & Vegetables	Fats & Oils	Extra	Page
Turkey Nuggets & Curry Dip *(Photo: p. 18)* ●		1 1/2	1/2			1 1/2		30
Garden Patch Pitas		1	1		1/2	1		31
Icy Yogurt Pops *(Photo: p. 18)*				1/2	1 1/2			32
Tomato Pan Bagna *(Photo: p. 18)*		1/2	1		1	1		33
Chicken Fingers	●	2	1/2			1/2		34
Pita Pita Hunger Beater	●	1	1			1	1	35
Tangy Taco Pups	●	2	1/2			2		36
Oven-Fried Onion Rings		1/2	1/2		1/2	2		37
Cheezy Bread Cube Snacks	●	2 1/2	1			1		38

The Food Choice Values on each recipe do not include accompanying foods which are suggested in many of the recipes and shown in some of the photographs.

Turkey Nuggets with Curry Dip

Cooking these nuggets in the microwave makes the meat juicy
and moist; and by making them yourself, you <u>know</u> that only quality
breast meat is used, unlike most fast food restaurant versions.

PHOTO ON PAGE 18.

50 mL	butter or soft margarine	3 tbsp
10 mL	honey	2 tsp
0.5 mL	dry mustard	1/8 tsp
500 g	turkey breast, cut in twenty-four 2.5 cm (1 inch) chunks	1 lb
125 mL	finely ground flaked corn cereal	1/2 cup
5 mL	chopped fresh parsley	1 tsp

CURRY DIP

50 mL	mayonnaise	1/4 cup
50 mL	sour cream	1/4 cup
5 mL	curry powder	1 tsp
25 mL	finely chopped mango chutney	2 tbsp

Curry Dip: In small bowl, combine mayonnaise, sour cream,
curry powder and chutney, mixing well; chill.

In microwaveable bowl, melt butter at High (100 % power) 30 to 40
seconds; stir in honey and mustard. In shallow dish, combine cereal
and parsley. Coat turkey with butter mixture; roll in crumbs to coat
evenly.

Arrange 12 chunks around edge of microwaveable rack. Cover with
waxed paper. Microwave at High 1-1/2 to 2 minutes.
Let stand 2 minutes. Repeat with remaining turkey. Serve with dip.

Makes 8 servings of 3 nuggets each (1 nugget = 28g/1 oz).

FOOD CHOICE VALUE *per serving*

Each Serving: 3 nuggets

1 1/2	☑ *Protein Choices*
1/2	☐ *Starchy Choice*
1 1/2	▲ *Fats & Oils Choices*

10 g	Carbohydrate
11 g	Protein
11 g	Total Fat
706	kilojoules (179 Calories)

Garden Patch Pitas

When is a sandwich not a sandwich? When it's a pita, of course. The popularity of pita bread for sandwiches is not hard to understand once you've had one. Each half of a pita bread round provides the perfect pocket to pack with luscious fillings.

50 mL	*mayonnaise*	*1/4 cup*
25 mL	*minced green onion*	*2 tbsp*
15 mL	*vinegar*	*1 tbsp*
1 mL	*dried dillweed*	*1/4 tsp*
375 mL	*cottage cheese*	*1 1/2 cups*
250 mL	*peeled, seeded, chopped cucumber*	*1 cup*
pinch	*Salt*	*pinch*
3	*pita breads, halved*	*3*
	Leaf lettuce	
6	*slices tomato*	*6*

Combine mayonnaise, onion, vinegar and dillweed; toss lightly with cottage cheese and cucumber in bowl. Season with salt to taste.

Line each pita bread half with lettuce; add tomato slice. Evenly divide cottage cheese mixture among pockets.

Makes 6 servings, of 1/2 pita (each 140 g/5 oz).

FOOD CHOICE VALUE *per serving*

Each Serving: 1/2 of pita

1	▨	*Protein Choice*
1	☐	*Starchy Choice*
1/2	◣	*Fruits & Vegetables Choice*
1	◥	*Fats & Oils Choice*

21 g	*Carbohydrate*
11 g	*Protein*
9 g	*Total Fat*
875	*kilojoules (209 Calories)*

Icy Yogurt Pops

Make different batches of these for a colorful array of tasty treats.
Try lemonade or limeade concentrate, tinted a pale yellow or green
if desired.

250 mL	*plain yogurt*	*1 cup*
175 mL	*frozen grape juice concentrate thawed**	*3/4 cup*
175 mL	*milk*	*3/4 cup*

In bowl, combine yogurt, grape juice concentrate and milk; divide
amoung six 100 mL (3 oz) paper cups. Freeze until partially frozen.

Insert wooden stick into centre of each pop; freeze until firm.
To serve, peel off paper.

Makes 6 servings.

PHOTO ON PAGE 18.

**Either lemonade concentrate
OR limeade concentrate may
be substituted,using the same
Food Choice Value.*

FOOD CHOICE VALUE *per serving*

Each Serving: 1 Yogurt Pop

1/2 ◆ *Milk Choice (2%)*

1 1/2 ▱ *Fruits & Vegetables Choices*

20 g	*Carbohydrate*
3 g	*Protein*
1 g	*Total Fat*
441	*kilojoules (105 Calories)*

Tomato Pan Bagna

PHOTO ON PAGE 18.

This sandwich originated in Provence, formerly a part of Italy. The ingredients from this area: tomatoes, garlic, green pepper, red wine vinegar and oil are therefore similar to those of Italy.

This toteable sandwich is like a salad in a sandwich. Served in crusty bread or rolls, it has been referred to as the "beach sandwich of Nice." Particulary nice in August and September when garden tomatoes are ripe and juicy.

4	medium tomatoes, chopped	4
1	medium sweet green pepper, chopped	1
125 mL	sliced radishes	1/2 cup
3	green onions, sliced	3
1	large clove garlic, minced	1
1	long French baguette (or 6 crusty rolls)	1
250 mL	shredded cooked chicken	1 cup
	DRESSING	
75 mL	vegetable oil	1/3 cup
25 mL	red wine vinegar	2 tbsp
2 mL	salt	1/2 tsp
1 mL	paprika	1/4 tsp
	Pepper	

In large bowl, combine tomatoes, green pepper, radishes, onions and garlic.

Dressing: Combine oil, vinegar, salt, paprika and pepper to taste; pour over vegetables. Refrigerate 30 minutes.

Cut bread in half lengthwise. Carefully pull out some bread from centre of each half, leaving 1 cm (1/2 inch) thick wall.

Using slotted spoon, put half salad mixture into lower half of baguette. Arrange chicken over salad; mound remaining salad over chicken. Place top half of bread over filling.

Tie at intervals with string. Wrap securely in foil and refrigerate for 3 hours. To serve, slice with bread knife into 5 cm (2 inch) thick slices.

Makes 12 servings using baguette and 6 to 12 servings using crusty rolls.

FOOD CHOICE VALUE *per serving*

Each Serving: 1/12 of baguette

1/2	☑ *Protein Choice*
1	☐ *Starchy Choice*
1	◨ *Fruits & Vegetables Choice*
1	◣ *Fats & Oils Choice*

25 g	*Carbohydrate*
8 g	*Protein*
7 g	*Total Fat*
794	*kilojoules (189 Calories)*

Chicken Fingers

These tender morsels turn out a lovely golden brown because you use a browning dish in the microwave. Kids love these either in lunches or as after school snacks.

2	*chicken breasts, skinned and boned*	*2*
1	*egg*	*1*
15 mL	*milk*	*1 tbsp*
125 mL	*fine dry bread crumbs*	*1/2 cup*
15 mL	*grated Parmesan cheese*	*1 tbsp*
2 mL	*crushed dried oregano*	*1/2 tsp*
30 mL	*vegetable oil*	*2 tbsp*

Cut chicken crosswise into strips about 1 cm (1/2 inch) thick.

Beat together egg and milk. Combine crumbs, cheese and oregano. Dip chicken into egg mixture, then into crumbs.

Preheat flat-bottomed browning dish 4 to 6 minutes. Add 15 mL (1 tbsp) of the oil and half the chicken. Microwave at High (100% power) 1 minute. Turn pieces over. Microwave at High 1 minute longer or until browned and chicken is no longer pink inside. Drain on paper towels. Repeat with remaining oil and chicken.

Makes 6 servings.

FOOD CHOICE VALUE	*per serving*
Each Serving: 6 fingers	
2	☑ *Protein Choices*
1/2	☐ *Starchy Choice*
1/2	▲ *Fats & Oils Choice*
8 g	*Carbohydrate*
14 g	*Protein*
8 g	*Total Fat*
703	*kilojoules (168 Calories)*

Pita Pita Hunger Beater

Use your microwave oven to whip up a satisfying lunch in seconds. Easy and fun to make at lunch break.

15 mL	*finely chopped onion*	1 tbsp
15 mL	*finely chopped sweet green pepper*	1 tbsp
15 mL	*finely chopped celery*	1 tbsp
5 mL	*butter*	1 tsp
2	*eggs*	2
25 mL	*milk*	2 tbsp
1	*pita bread, cut in half*	1

In 1 L (4 cup) glass measuring cup, combine onion, green pepper, celery and butter. Microwave at High (100% power) for 1 minute 30 seconds.

Add eggs and milk; mix well with fork. Cover with vented plastic wrap. Microwave at High for 80 or 90 seconds or until almost set, stirring once halfway through cooking. Let stand 2 minutes, still covered.

Meanwhile, wrap pita bread in paper towel; microwave at Medium (50% power) for 20 seconds. Divide scrambled eggs evenly between pita bread pockets.

Makes 2 servings.

FOOD CHOICE VALUE	*per serving*
Each Serving: 1/2 of pita bread	
1	☑ *Protein Choice*
1	☐ *Starchy Choice*
1	▲ *Fats & Oils Choice*
1	➕ *Extra*
18 g	*Carbohydrate*
9 g	*Protein*
7 g	*Total Fat*
382	*kilojoules (174 Calories)*

Tangy Taco Pups

Garnish each serving with shredded lettuce, finely chopped tomato and green onion. Serve with Nacho Chips and Tomato Salsa (page 40).

2 mL	*butter or soft margarine*	*1/2 tsp*
2	*eggs*	*2*
25 mL	*chopped onion*	*2 tbsp*
25 mL	*water*	*2 tbsp*
25 mL	*shredded part-skim Cheddar cheese*	*2 tbsp*
2	*wieners*	*2*
2	*taco shells*	*2*
10 mL	*mild taco sauce or ketchup*	*2 tsp*

In microwaveable bowl, microwave butter at High (100% power) for 15 seconds until melted. Add eggs, onion and water; beat together with fork. Cover with vented plastic wrap. Microwave at High for 50 to 80 seconds or until almost set, stirring twice during cooking time. Mix in shredded cheese. Set aside.

Pierce wieners with fork. Place one wiener in each taco shell. Stand taco shells upright in dish, supporting them with crumpled waxed paper. Spoon equal amounts of scrambled eggs into each taco shell; drizzle with taco sauce. Microwave at High for 1 minute until heated through.

Makes 2 servings.

FOOD CHOICE VALUE	*per serving*
Each Serving: 1 taco	
2	☑ *Protein Choices*
1/2	☐ *Starchy Choice*
2	▲ *Fats & Oils Choices*

9 g	*Carbohydrate*
14 g	*Protein*
17 g	*Total Fat*
817	*kilojoules (245 Calories)*

Oven-Fried Onion Rings

Kids love onion rings, but mothers don't like them to have all that fat. For a low-fat but crispy, flavorful version, try these easy oven-fried rings. They're great with homemade hamburgers.

3	*onions, cut in 5 mm (1/4-inch) slices and separated into rings*	*3*
250 mL	*buttermilk*	*1 cup*
50 mL	*all-purpose flour*	*1/4 cup*
50 mL	*freshly grated Parmesan cheese*	*1/4 cup*
25 mL	*dried parsley*	*2 tbsp*
1 mL	*pepper*	*1/4 tsp*
pinch	*Salt*	*pinch*
50 mL	*butter*	*1/4 cup*

In sturdy plastic bag, combine onion rings with buttermilk; close tightly and let stand at room temperature for 30 minutes. In another plastic bag, shake together flour, cheese, parsley, pepper, and salt to taste.

In large jelly roll pan, melt butter. Drain onions in strainer and drop, a few at a time, into flour mixture. Shake to coat and place in single layer in pan. Bake in 190°C (375°F) oven for 30 minutes or until tender inside and crisp outside, carefully turning once with lifter.

Makes 4 servings.

KID'S FAVORITE

If you don't have any buttermilk on hand, you can substitute sour milk. Just mix 15 mL (1 tbsp) vinegar into 250 mL (1 cup) 2% milk and let stand for 15 minutes before using.

FOOD CHOICE VALUE *per serving*

Each Serving: 1/4 of recipe

1/2	◪ *Protein Choice*
1/2	◻ *Starchy Choice*
1/2	◪ *Fruits & Vegetables Choice*
2	◤ *Fats & Oils Choices*
15 g	*Carbohydrate*
6 g	*Protein*
11 g	*Total Fat*
752	*kilojoules (179 Calories)*

FOODLAND ONTARIO

Cheezy Bread Cube Snacks

A different "Make-Ahead" snack of little tidbits. These make a great side dish for lunch or anytime snacks for hungry little appetites.

500 mL	*bread cubes (about 3 slices)*	*2 cups*
250 mL	*part-skim shredded Cheddar cheese*	*1 cup*
2	*green onions, finely chopped*	*2*
4	*eggs*	*4*
375 mL	*milk*	*1 1/2 cups*
1 mL	*salt*	*1/4 tsp*
Pinch	*pepper*	*Pinch*
1	*tomato, cut in wedges*	*1*

Divide half of the bread cubes among 6 microwaveable cereal bowls or place in 25 cm (10 inch) pie plate. Sprinkle evenly with about half of the cheese. Divide green onions among dishes. Top each with remaining bread cubes and cheese.

Beat eggs with milk, salt and pepper; pour over bread cube mixture. Cover each with plastic wrap; put in the refrigerater for several hours or overnight.

Vent plastic wrap on each dish. Microwave at Medium (50% power) for 17 minutes, rotating dishes once during cooking time. Let stand, covered, for 5 minutes. Garnish with tomato wedge.

Makes 6 servings.

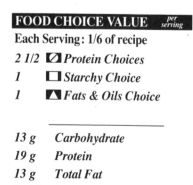

FOOD CHOICE VALUE	*per serving*
Each Serving: 1/6 of recipe	

2 1/2	☑	*Protein Choices*
1	☐	*Starchy Choice*
1	▲	*Fats & Oils Choice*

13 g	*Carbohydrate*
19 g	*Protein*
13 g	*Total Fat*
1016	*kilojoules (242 Calories)*

APPETIZERS

	 Microwave	Protein	Starchy	Fruits & Vegetables	Fats & Oils	Extra	Page
Two-Step Tomato Salsa						1	40
Orchard Fresh Devils		1			1/2		41
Mini Cocktail Meatballs		1 1/2					42
Cocktail Chickenballs		1/2			1/2		43
Steamed Mussels Appetizer	●	1		1	1		44
Mushroom and Leek Tart	●	1	1/2		1 1/2		45
Quick Mini Quiche		1 1/2	2		1		46
Savory Meatballs	●	1					47
Porky Pines *(Photo: p. 51)*		1	1/2				48
Creamy Herb Dip *(Photo: p. 51)*					1		49
Ham and Gouda en Croute *(Photo: p. 51)*		1	1/2		1		50

The Food Choice Values on each recipe do not include accompanying foods which are suggested in many of the recipes and shown in some of the photographs.

Two-Step Tomato Salsa

Easy to prepare and keep on hand, this zesty dip is perfect with nacho chips or pita pockets. Years ago as a child, I remember a boy who brought vegetables, salsa and tortilla chips for lunch. The lunch was nutritious and the envy of his class-mates. Don't be shy in helping your children discover the flavor of seasoned food...but start slow. Children's taste buds are more acute than adult's. Younger children usually like their food quite plain, so judge your child's tastes accordingly.

1	*can (398 mL/14 oz) tomatoes (undrained)*	*1*
Half	*small onion, finely chopped*	*Half*
1	*clove garlic, minced*	*1*
25 mL	*chopped fresh parsley*	*2 tbsp*
	(or 15 mL/1 tbsp dried), optional	
2 mL	*each chili powder and dried oregano*	*1/2 tsp*
Dash	*hot pepper sauce*	*Dash*
Pinch	*granulated sugar*	*Pinch*
	Salt and pepper	

You can store this salsa in the refrigerator for up to 3 days.

In bowl, crush tomatoes to chunky purée with potato masher. Stir in onion, garlic, parsley (if using), chili powder, oregano, hot pepper sauce, sugar, and salt and pepper to taste.

Makes about 500 mL (2 cups).

FOOD CHOICE VALUE *per serving*

Each Serving: 25 mL (2 tbsp)

1 **++** *Extra*

1 g	*Carbohydrate*
0 g	*Protein*
0 g	*Total Fat*
17	*kilojoules (4 Calories)*

Orchard Fresh Devils

Bland foods served hot or cold, seasoned with cayenne, paprika and other spicy ingredients and mixed with a dressing of mayonnaise, wine or vinegar are foods we describe as devilled. Eggs are one of the easiest and most delicious devilled treats. Here's a new and refreshing twist for devilled eggs.

6	*hard-cooked eggs, peeled and halved lengthwise*	6
50 mL	*plain low-fat yogurt*	3 tbsp
15 mL	*minced unpeeled red or green apple*	1 tbsp
15 mL	*minced celery*	1 tbsp
15 mL	*finely chopped pecans, almonds or walnuts*	1 tbsp
5 mL	*lime or lemon juice*	1 tsp
1 mL	*salt*	1/4 tsp
Pinch	*curry powder (optional)*	Pinch

Remove yolks; set whites aside. In bowl, mash yolks with fork. Blend in yogurt, apple, celery, nuts, lime juice, salt, and curry powder (if using).

Fill whites, using heaping 5 mL (1 tsp) of yolk mixture in each half. Cover and refrigerate until chilled.

Makes 6 servings.

FOOD CHOICE VALUE *per serving*

Each Serving: 2 egg halves

1 ◪ *Protein Choice*

1/2 ◣ *Fats & Oils Choice*

2 g	*Carbohydrate*
7 g	*Protein*
6 g	*Total Fat*
374	*kilojoules (89 Calories)*

Mini Cocktail Meatballs

The tangy taste of raspberries adds zest to this hearty cocktail party staple. Serve the cooked meatballs in a chafing dish to keep them warm throughout the festivities. Serve alongside a plate of crunchy vegetable pieces.

500 g	extra-lean ground beef	1 lb
125 mL	fresh bread crumbs	1/2 cup
1	egg, beaten	1
25 mL	tomato sauce	2 tbsp
25 mL	finelychopped onion	2 tbsp
15 mL	powdered beef bouillon mix	1 tbsp
5 mL	Worcestershire sauce	1 tsp
1 mL	garlic salt	1/4 tsp
50 mL	no-sugar-added raspberry spread	1/4 cup
50 mL	chili sauce	1/4 cup

In large bowl, combine beef, bread crumbs, egg, tomato sauce, onion, bouillon mix, Worcestershire sauce and salt; mix well. Using 5 mL (1 tsp), form into 80 meatballs. Place on nonstick jelly roll pan. Bake in 200°C (400°F) oven 10 to 12 minutes or until no longer pink inside. Drain fat.

In large saucepan, combine raspberry spread and chili sauce. Cook, stirring over low heat until smoothly combined. Add meatballs and heat through.

Makes 80 mini meatballs.

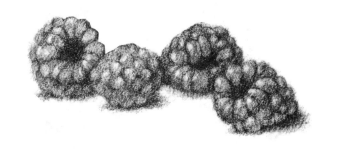

FOOD CHOICE VALUE *per serving*

Each Serving: 8 mini meatballs

1 1/2 ☑ *Protein Choices*

3 g	*Carbohydrate*
10 g	*Protein*
5 g	*Total Fat*
408	*kilojoules (98 Calories)*

Cocktail Chicken Balls

Start the evening right with these tasty morsels. Serve alongside a crunchy plate of vegetable pieces and creamy herb dip (page 49).

500 g	*ground chicken*	*1 lb*
2	*eggs, beaten*	*2*
125 mL	*bread crumbs*	*1/2 cup*
25 mL	*grated Parmesan cheese*	*2 tbsp*
15 mL	*dried parsley*	*1 tbsp*
10 mL	*dried basil*	*2 tsp*
10 mL	*dried oregano*	*2 tsp*
2 mL	*garlic powder*	*1/2 tsp*
1 mL	*pepper*	*1/4 tsp*
30mL	*Peanut oil*	*2 tbsp*

In bowl, combine chicken, eggs, bread crumbs, cheese, parsley, basil, oregano, garlic and pepper; shape into 2.5 cm (1-inch) balls.

Pour oil into a skillet to depth of 3 mm (1/8 inch); heat over medium heat. Cook chicken balls, in batches, for about 10 minutes or until golden and no longer pink inside.

Makes 4 dozen.

Prepare Ahead

You can prepare these ahead of time to refrigerate for up to two days. Just reheat them before serving.

FOOD CHOICE VALUE *per serving*

Each Serving: 2 Chicken Balls

1/2 ◪ *Protein Choice*

1/2 ◩ *Fats & Oils Choice*

2 g	*Carbohydrate*
4 g	*Protein*
4 g	*Total Fat*
260	*kilojoules (62 Calories)*

Steamed Mussels Appetizer

This recipe is inexpensive, easy to prepare, and boasts a textured taste, steeped in maritime goodness. Serve with Italian-style bread to soak up all the hearty juices.

1.5 kg	*mussels (5 to 6 dozen)*	*3 lb*
25 mL	*vegetable oil*	*2 tbsp*
50 mL	*chopped onion*	*1/4 cup*
1	*clove garlic, minced*	*1*
450 mL	*spaghetti sauce*	*1 3/4 cups*
75 mL	*Chablis or other dry white wine**	*1/3 cup*

Discard any mussels that do not close when lightly tapped. Scrub mussels under cold running water; remove and discard beards.

In 4 L (16 cup) microwaveable casserole, combine oil and onion. Cover and microwave at High (100% power) 4 minutes or until onion is tender, stirring once.

Stir in spaghetti sauce and Chablis; cover and microwave at High 3 minutes or until hot and bubbling.

Stir in mussels. Cover and microwave at High 4 minutes or until mussels open, stirring once.

Discard any unopened mussels.

Makes 8 servings.

MICROWAVEABLE

GOOD Source of IRON

*Ask your dietitian or doctor about the use of alcohol.

FOOD CHOICE VALUE	*per serving*

Each Serving: 1/8 of recipe

1	◨ *Protein Choice*
1	◧ *Fruits & Vegetables Choice*
1	◣ *Fats & Oils Choice*

12 g	*Carbohydrate*
8 g	*Protein*
7 g	*Total Fat*
609	*kilojoules (145 Calories)*

Mushroom and Leek Tart

As well as an easy appetizer, this also makes a wonderful lunch when served with a crispy, fresh green salad.

Be sure to remove sand from leeks before chopping. To clean leeks, simply cut them in half lengthwise and rinse away sand with running water.

15 mL	butter or soft margarine	1 tbsp
500 mL	finely chopped leeks	2 cups
375 mL	sliced fresh mushrooms	1 1/2 cups
1	can (284 mL/10 oz) condensed cream of celery soup	1
4	eggs, beaten	4
250 mL	shredded Swiss cheese	1 cup
125 mL	half-and-half cream (10% fat)	1/2 cup
15 mL	all-purpose flour	1 tbsp
Pinch	nutmeg	Pinch
Pinch	cayenne pepper	Pinch

In 2 L (8-cup) microwaveable casserole, combine butter, leeks and mushrooms. Cover with lid; microwave at High (100% power) 6 minutes or until vegetables are tender, stirring once during cooking. Spoon off any excess liquid.

In bowl, stir soup until smooth. Stir in leek mixture, eggs, cheese, half-and-half, flour, nutmeg and cayenne until well blended. Pour into 23 cm (9-inch) microwaveable pie plate.

Microwave, uncovered, at Medium (50% power) 22 minutes or until centre is nearly set, rotating dish 3 times during cooking. Let stand 10 minutes before serving.

Makes 8 servings.

FOOD CHOICE VALUE *per serving*

Each Serving: 1/8 of recipe

1	☑ *Protein Choice*
1/2	☐ *Starchy Choice*
1 1/2	▲ *Fats & Oils Choice*

9 g	Carbohydrate
9 g	Protein
11 g	Total Fat
730	kilojoules *(174 Calories)*

Quick Mini Quiche

A mini treat that provides maxi taste. This fun to make recipe is great for simple party hors d'oeuvres or anytime snacks. Serve alongside carrot and zucchini sticks.

18	*slices fresh bread, crusts removed*	*18*
	Butter or soft margarine	
8	*eggs, beaten*	*8*
250 mL	*milk*	*1 cup*
125 mL	*low-fat plain yogurt*	*1/2 cup*
	Pepper	
4	*slices back bacon, chopped*	*4*
125 mL	*finely chopped green onion*	*1/2 cup*
125 mL	*shredded part-skim Cheddar cheese*	*1/2 cup*
	Chopped fresh parsley	

Spread bread lightly with butter; press firmly, buttered side down, into 18 muffin tins. Bake in 160°C (325°F) oven for 10 minutes.

Meanwhile, in pitcher, combine eggs, milk, yogurt, and pepper to taste. Set aside. In a skillet, sauté bacon and onion until bacon is crisp and onion softened.

Divide bacon mixture among bread cups. Pour some of the egg mixture over top; let partially absorb. Pour in remaining egg mixture; sprinkle with cheese.

Bake for 30 minutes or until golden and puffed. If edges of bread start to brown before eggs are set, cover with foil. Garnish with parsley.

Makes 9 servings, each of 2 Mini Quiche.

FOOD CHOICE VALUE *per serving*

Each Serving: 2 Mini Quiche

1 1/2 ☑ *Protein Choices*

2 ☐ *Starchy Choices*

1 ▲ *Fats & Oils Choice*

29 g	*Carbohydrate*
16 g	*Protein*
10 g	*Total Fat*
1146	*kilojoules (274 Calories)*

Savory Meatballs

Add to your favorite spaghetti sauce, skewer with cocktail picks for hors d'oeuvres, slice and serve on crusty buns. These delicious meatballs have a multitude of culinary variations.

Meatballs can be cooked and frozen for up to 3 months.

750 g	*lean ground pork*	*1 1/2 lb*
125 mL	*rolled oats*	*1/2 cup*
50 mL	*milk*	*1/4 cup*
2	*cloves garlic, minced*	*2*
1	*egg, beaten*	*1*
2 mL	*salt*	*1/2 tsp*
1 mL	*pepper*	*1/4 tsp*

In bowl, combine pork, rolled oats, milk, garlic, egg, salt and pepper; shape into 2.5 cm (1-inch) balls.

Arrange one-third of the meatballs about 1 cm (1/2-inch) apart, in 23 cm (9-inch) microwaveable pie plate. Cover dish with vented plastic wrap. Microwave at High (100% power) for 3 to 4 minutes or until no longer pink inside, rotating the dish halfway through cooking time. Let stand, covered, for 2 minutes. Drain excess liquid. Repeat with remaining meatballs.

Makes 50 meatballs.

FOOD CHOICE VALUE *per serving*

Each Serving: 2 Meatballs

1 ☑*Protein Choice*

1 g	*Carbohydrate*
6 g	*Protein*
4 g	*Total Fat*
269	*kilojoules (64 Calories)*

■   ■ ■ ■ ■ ■ ■ ■ ■ ■ ■ ■ ■ ■ ■

Porky Pines

Serve these hot tender morsels with your favorite dipping sauce.

500 g	lean boneless pork (shoulder, loin or leg)	1 lb
1	egg	1
15 mL	water	1 tbsp
250 mL	cracker crumbs	1 cup
25 mL	minced fresh parsley	2 tbsp
15 mL	grated Parmesan cheese	1 tbsp
2 mL	seasoned salt	1/2 tsp
2 mL	Italian seasoning	1/2 tsp
Pinch	sage (optional)	Pinch
Pinch	granulated sugar	Pinch

Cut pork across the grain into 5 mm (1/4 inch) thick slices; cut into 5 x 2 cm (2 x 3/4 inch) fingers. In small bowl, combine egg and water. In separate bowl, combine cracker crumbs, parsley, cheese, seasoned salt, Italian seasoning, sage (if using) and sugar.

Dip each pork finger into egg, then crumb mixture. Place fingers on lightly greased baking sheet. Bake in 190°C (375°F) oven for 20 minutes.

Makes about 2 dozen.

PHOTO ON PAGE 51.

Try with Tomato Salsa recipe on page 40, or Creamy Herb Dip on next page.

FOOD CHOICE VALUE *per serving*

Each Serving: 2 fingers

1   ☑ *Protein Choice*

1/2   ☐ *Starchy Choice*

6 g	Carbohydrate
10 g	Protein
4 g	Total Fat
386	kilojoules (92 Calories)

Creamy Herb Dip

PHOTO ON PAGE 51.

Whether for the armchair coach or hungry children, this dip will satisfy everyone. Serve with crisp vegetables or crackers for dipping.

125 g	*cream cheese, softened*	*1 pkg*
175 mL	*plain yogurt*	*3/4 cup*
15 mL	*finely chopped green onion*	*1 tbsp*
15 mL	*finely chopped fresh parsley*	*1 tbsp*
5 mL	*dried dillweed*	*1 tsp*
	Seasoned salt	

In bowl, beat cream cheese until smooth; gradually beat in yogurt.

Stir in onion, parsley and dillweed. Add seasoned salt to taste. Chill at least 1 hour to blend flavors.

Makes about 400 mL (1 2/3 cups).

Variation: Creamy Seafood Dip: Omit parsley and dillweed. Add 5 mL (1 tsp) prepared horseradish, 4 mL (3/4 tsp) Worcestershire sauce and 1 mL (1/4 tsp) hot pepper sauce. Stir in 250 mL (1 cup) drained, flaked crab meat or finely chopped cooked shrimp. Makes about 500 mL (2 cups).

For this seafood variation, add 1/2 ◨ *Protein Choice to base recipe, for 25 mL (2 tbsp) serving.*

FOOD CHOICE VALUE *per serving*

Each Serving: 25 mL (2 tbsp)

1 ▲ *Fats & Oils Choice*

---

1 g	*Carbohydrate*
2 g	*Protein*
4 g	*Total Fat*
176	*kilojoules (42 Calories)*

Ham and Gouda en Croûte

Thin slices of a tasty ham mixture encircled with French bread crust is a delicious make-ahead hors d'oeuvre.

PHOTO ON PAGE 51.

2	*cans (each 184 g/6.5 oz) flaked ham, drained*	2
500 mL	*shredded Gouda cheese*	*2 cups*
25 mL	*chopped green onion*	*2 tbsp*
15 mL	*chopped fresh parsley*	*1 tbsp*
10 mL	*prepared mustard*	*2 tsp*
5 mL	*Worcestershire sauce*	*1 tsp*
1	*baguette (French stick) 6 cm (2 1/2 inches) wide*	*1*

In bowl, thoroughly combine ham, cheese, onion, parsley, mustard and Worcestershire sauce.

Slice off ends of bread so loaf is 40 cm (16 inches) long. Hollow out loaf, leaving crust about 5 mm (1/4-inch) thick.

Stand loaf on one end; pack ham mixture into hollow. Wrap and refrigerate until chilled. Cut into 5 mm (1/4-inch) thick slices.

Makes 64 slices.

FOOD CHOICE VALUE *per serving*

Each Serving: 4 slices

1	▨ *Protein Choice*
1/2	☐ *Starchy Choice*
1	▲ *Fats & Oils Choice*

10 g	*Carbohydrate*
9 g	*Protein*
9 g	*Total Fat*
651	*kilojoules (155 Calories)*

Creamy Herb Dip (p.49)

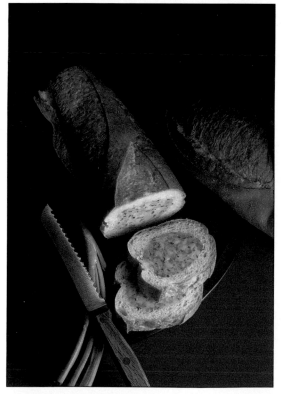

Ham and Gouda en Croute (p.50)   *Porky Pines (p.48)*

Chicken Minestrone (p.56)

Fresh Tomato & Dill Soup (p.59)

Budget-Wise Bouillabaisse (p.57)

Chunky Tomato Soup with Yogurt (p.58)

Garden Party Gazpacho (p.60)

Tostada Turkey Salad (p.71)

Thai Beef Salad (p.73)

SOUPS

	Microwave	Protein	Starchy	Fruits & Vegetables	Fats & Oils	Extra	Page
Chicken Minestrone (*Photo: p. 52*)		4	2	1			56
Budget-Wise Bouillabaisse (*Photo: p. 53*)		3	1	1			57
Chunky Tomato Soup & Yogurt (*Photo: p. 53*)		1/2		1	1 1/2		58
Fresh Tomato & Dill Soup (*Photo: p. 53*)				1/2			59
Garden Party Gazpacho (*Photo: p. 53*)		1		1			60
Chili Chowder		1/2	1 1/2	1	1/2		61
Chilly Tomato Bisque		1/2		1			62
Broccoli & Cauliflower Soup		1	1/2	1 1/2			63
Broccoli Squash Soup		1/2		1		1	64
Fundy Bay Clam Chowder		3		1	1		65
Egg Drop Soup		1 1/2					66
Cauliflower Lentil Soup		1	1	1		1	67
Mushroom Tomato Pasta Soup		2	1 1/2	1	2		68
Cucumber Leek Soup	●	1		1			69

The Food Choice Values on each recipe do not include accompanying foods which are suggested in many of the recipes and shown in some of the photographs.

Chicken Minestrone

Typically, minestrone is a heart-warming beef-based vegetable soup with many variations. Here, chicken is used instead of beef.

25 mL	vegetable oil	2 tbsp
375 g	boneless skinless chicken breasts, cut into 2.5 cm (1-inch) slivers	3/4 lb
2	medium carrots, chopped	2
1	medium onion, chopped	1
125 mL	chopped celery	1/2 cup
1	can (540 mL/19 oz)* tomatoes with spices	1
1	can (284 mL/10 oz) chicken broth, plus 1 can water	1
2 mL	dried thyme	1/2 tsp
1 mL	dried rosemary, crumbled	1/4 tsp
1	can (398 mL/14 oz) kidney beans, drained	1
175 mL	macaroni	3/4 cup

In large saucepan, heat oil over medium heat; sauté chicken, carrots, onion and celery about 5 minutes or until tender.

Add tomatoes, breaking up with fork. Add chicken broth and water, thyme and rosemary; bring to boil. Reduce heat, cover and simmer 10 minutes.

Stir in kidney beans and macaroni; simmer, uncovered, 10 to 12 minutes, stirring occasionally, or until macaroni is tender.

Makes 4 servings, each 450 mL/15 oz.

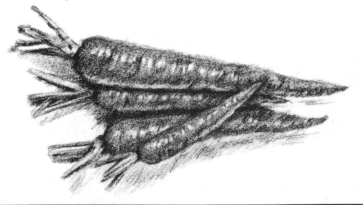

PHOTO ON PAGE 52.

HIGH FIBRE

*Recipe has been developed for use with 19 oz or 28 oz can sizes. Nutritional analysis based on 19 oz size only.

FOOD CHOICE VALUE *per serving*

Each Serving: 1/4 of recipe

4	☑	*Protein Choices*
2	☐	*Starchy Choices*
1	◪	*Fruits & Vegetables Choice*

49 g	*Carbohydrate*
33 g	*Protein*
3 g	*Total Fat*
1147	*kilojoules (273 Calories)*

Budget-Wise Bouillabaisse

PHOTO ON PAGE 53.

This wonderfully flavored soup could use a variety of fish to suit your taste. It could also be served over pasta, if desired.

*Recipe has been developed for use with 19 oz or 28 oz can sizes. Nutritional analysis based on 19 oz size only.

†Ask your dietitian or doctor about the use of alcohol.

To be even more economical, omit the shrimp in this bountiful Mediterranean fish stew. Use a mixture of white fish and serve over pasta.

25 mL	*olive oil*	2 tbsp
3	*leeks (white parts only), sliced*	3
1	*clove garlic, minced*	1
1	*can (540 mL / 19 oz)* tomatoes with spices*	1
125 mL	*dry white wine† or chicken broth*	1/2 cup
1	*large potato, peeled and cubed*	1
5 mL	*dried basil*	1 tsp
5 mL	*Worcestershire sauce*	1 tsp
1 mL	*dried dillweed*	1/4 tsp
250 g	*fish fillets (haddock, sole, cod), cut into 2.5 cm (1 inch) cubes*	1/2 lb
250 g	*cooked shrimp*	1/2 lb

In large saucepan, heat oil over medium heat; sauté leeks for 4 minutes. Add garlic and sauté 1 minute longer.

Stir in tomatoes, breaking up with a fork. Add wine, potato, basil, Worcestershire sauce and dillweed; bring to boil. Reduce heat, cover and simmer 15 minutes or until potatoes are tender.

Add fish; simmer, uncovered, 5 minutes or until fish flakes easily when tested with fork. Add shrimp and heat through.

Makes 4 servings, each 390 mL/13oz.

FOOD CHOICE VALUE *per serving*

Each Serving: 1/4 of recipe

3	☑ *Protein Choices*
1	☐ *Starchy Choice*
1	☑ *Fruits & Vegetables Choice*

25 g	*Carbohydrate*
25 g	*Protein*
10 g	*Total Fat*
1201	*kilojoules (286 Calories)*

Chunky Tomato Soup with Herbed Yogurt

A hint of orange and the savory addition of basil herbed yogurt creates a rich-tasting version of this staple soup. Easy to prepare ahead of time and re-heat when company arrives.

15 mL	*vegetable oil*	*1 tbsp*
1	*large onion, chopped*	*1*
1	*clove garlic, minced*	*1*
5 mL	*grated orange rind*	*1 tsp*
1	*can (540 mL/19 oz)* tomatoes*	*1*
375 mL	*chicken broth*	*1 1/2 cups*
1 mL	*dried thyme*	*1/4 tsp*

HERBED YOGURT

125 mL	*plain low-fat yogurt*	*1/2 cup*
1	*green onion, chopped*	*1*
10 mL	*dried basil*	*2 tsp*

Herbed Yogurt: Combine plain yogurt, green onion and 5 mL (1 tsp) of the basil; cover and refrigerate. In saucepan, heat oil over medium heat; sauté onion, garlic and orange rind for 3 minutes. Stir in tomatoes, breaking up with fork.

Add chicken broth, remaining basil and thyme; bring to boil. Reduce heat, cover and simmer 20 minutes. Serve topped with herbed yogurt.

Makes 4 servings, each 280g/10 oz.

PHOTO ON PAGE 53.

Prepare Ahead

Basil is sometimes called the "tomato herb" and may be used in most Tomato recipes. Basil blends well with other herbs in seasoning foods. Suggested amounts to use: -1/4 to 1/2 tsp in 2 cups green vegetables. -3/4 to 1 1/2 tsp for 1 1/2 lbs pork chops or roasts.

*Recipe has been developed for use with 19 oz or 28 oz can sizes. Nutritional analysis based on 19 oz size only.

FOOD CHOICE VALUE	*per serving*
Each Serving: 1/4 of recipe	
1/2 ☑ *Protein Choice*	
1 ◪ *Fruits & Vegetables Choice*	
1 1/2 ◣ *Fats & Oils Choices*	

10 g	*Carbohydrate*
4 g	*Protein*
8 g	*Total Fat*
546	*kilojoules (130 Calories)*

Soups

Fresh Tomato and Dill Soup

PHOTO ON PAGE 53.

For an attractive presentation, swirl a spoonful of plain yogurt into each serving just enough to leave white streaks.

This soup, flavored with the stimulating taste of dill and the freshness of vine-ripened tomatoes, needs no cooking and makes an excellent refresher for a hot summer day.

3	large tomatoes, peeled and chopped	3
125 mL	plain low-fat yogurt	1/2 cup
15 mL	chopped fresh dill (or 5 mL/1 tsp dried dillweed)	1 tbsp
1 mL	salt	1/4 tsp
0.5 mL	pepper	1/8 tsp
25 mL	chopped green onions	2 tbsp
	Chopped tomatoes	
	Fresh dill	

In blender or food processor, purée tomatoes, yogurt, dill, salt and pepper until smooth. Stir in green onions and chill at least 2 hours.

Ladle into bowls; garnish with chopped tomatoes and fresh dill.

Makes 4 servings.

FOOD CHOICE VALUE *per serving*

Each Serving: 1/4 of recipe

1/2 **☐** *Fruits & Vegetables Choice*

7 g	Carbohydrate
2 g	Protein
1 g	Total Fat
181	kilojoules (43 Calories)

Garden Party Gazpacho

This simple soup will only improve as the flavors blend together while being chilled. Serve alongside a plate of sliced cucumbers, tomatoes and basket of Nacho chips.

PHOTO ON PAGE 53.

625 mL	*tomato juice*	*2 1/2 cups*
50 mL	*red wine vinegar*	*1/4 cup*
7 mL	*salt*	*1 1/2 tsp*
4 mL	*Worcestershire sauce*	*3/4 tsp*
3	*green onions, chopped*	*3*
1	*clove garlic*	*1*
250 mL	*peeled, seeded, chopped , cucumber*	*1 cup*
250 mL	*chopped sweet green pepper*	*1 cup*
250 mL	*cottage cheese*	*1 cup*

In blender, combine tomato juice, vinegar, salt, Worcestershire sauce, onions, garlic, half of the cucumber and half of the green pepper. Blend at medium speed until smooth. Cover and refrigerate for several hours or until chilled and flavors have blended.

To serve, ladle into bowls; top each serving with 1/4 cup of cottage cheese. Sprinkle with remaining cucumber and green pepper.

Makes 4 servings.

FOOD CHOICE VALUE *per serving*

Each Serving: 1/4 of recipe

1	☑	*Protein Choice*
1	◨	*Fruits & Vegetables Choice*

12 g	*Carbohydrate*
9 g	*Protein*
1 g	*Total Fat*
382	*kilojoules (91 Calories)*

Chili Chowder

This winter staple offers zesty south-of-the-border appeal.
Serve with shredded part-skim Cheddar cheese accompanied with
tortilla chips.

*For convenience and speed, it
helps to have quantities of chopped
onions and green pepper ready
and waiting in the freezer.*

**Recipe has been developed
for use with 19 oz or 28 oz can
sizes. Nutritional analysis
based on 19 oz size only.*

25 mL	*vegetable oil*	*2 tbsp*
1	*medium onion, chopped*	*1*
1	*medium sweet green pepper, chopped*	*1*
1	*can (540 mL / 19 oz)* Mexican spice stewed tomatoes*	*1*
250 mL	*chicken broth*	*1 cup*
5 mL	*chili powder*	*1 tsp*
1	*can (398 mL / 14 oz) red kidney beans (undrained)*	*1*
1	*can (341 mL / 12 oz) corn (undrained)*	

In large saucepan, heat oil over medium heat; sauté onion and
green pepper for 3 minutes.

Stir in tomatoes, chicken broth and chili powder; bring to boil.
Reduce heat, cover and simmer for 5 minutes.

Add undrained kidney beans and corn; cook, covered, 5 minutes
longer, stirring occasionally.

Makes 6 servings.

HIGH FIBRE

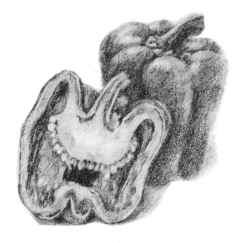

FOOD CHOICE VALUE <small>per serving</small>

Each Serving: 1/6 of recipe

- 1/2 ☑ *Protein Choice*
- 1 1/2 ☐ *Starchy Choices*
- 1 ◩ *Fruits & Vegetables Choice*
- 1/2 ◣ *Fats & Oils Choice*

- 32 g *Carbohydrate*
- 8 g *Protein*
- 6 g *Total Fat*
- 764 *kilojoules* (182 Calories)

Chilly Tomato Bisque Soup

A wonderful refreshing twist for a hot summer day. The vegetable juice, basil and tomatoes provide a unique blend of savory tomato flavor, while the yogurt offers a rich creamy consistency.

375 mL	vegetable juice cocktail	1 1/2 cups
250 mL	plain yogurt	250 mL
4	medium tomatoes; peeled, seeded	4
5 mL	basil	1 tsp
2 mL	salt	1/2 tsp
1 mL	pepper	1/4 tsp

In a blender container, combine vegetable juice cocktail, yogurt, 4 tomatoes, basil, salt and pepper. Cover and blend at medium speed until smooth. Cover and refrigerate several hours to blend flavors.

Serve well chilled. Garnish if desired.

Makes 4 servings, 250 mL (1 cup) each

FOOD CHOICE VALUE *per serving*

Each Serving: 250 mL (1 cup)

1/2 ☑ *Protein Choice*

1 ◪ *Fruits & Vegetables Choice*

14 g	Carbohydrate
5 g	Protein
1 g	Total Fat
328	kilojoules (78 Calories)

Broccoli and Cauliflower Soup

Crisp fresh broccoli and cauliflower combine with crunchy wild rice for a soup that's full of flavor and packs a healthy punch of fibre and nutrients.

750 mL	*chicken stock*	*3 cups*
125 mL	*wild rice, rinsed*	*1/2 cup*
1	*medium leek (white part only) halved lengthwise and thinly sliced*	*1*
1	*medium carrot, diced*	*1*
1	*bay leaf*	*1*
500 mL	*chopped cauliflower*	*2 cups*
500 mL	*chopped broccoli*	*2 cups*
5 mL	*Worcestershire sauce*	*1 tsp*
	Salt and pepper	

In large saucepan over high heat, bring stock to boil. Add wild rice; reduce heat to simmer and cook for 10 minutes.

Add leek, carrot and bay leaf; simmer for 5 minutes. Add cauliflower; simmer for 2 minutes. Add broccoli and Worcestershire sauce. Simmer for 3 minutes or until vegetables are just tender.

Discard bay leaf. Season to taste with salt and pepper. Serve immediately.

Makes 4 servings

FOOD CHOICE VALUE *per serving*

Each Serving: 1/4 of recipe

1	▨ *Protein Choice*
1/2	☐ *Starchy Choice*
1 1/2	◪ *Fruits & Vegetables Choices*

23 g	*Carbohydrate*
9 g	*Protein*
1 g	*Total Fat*
567	*kilojoules (135 Calories)*

FOODLAND ONTARIO

Broccoli Squash Soup

An unusual combination of broccoli and squash makes this creamy smooth soup extra nutritious. Add just a little dash of hot pepper sauce for a special zip.

500 mL	*coarsely chopped peeled butternut or acorn squash*	2 cups
250 mL	*chopped peeled broccoli stalks*	1 cup
1	*medium tomato, peeled and seeded*	1
750 mL	*chicken stock*	3 cups
500 mL	*small broccoli florets*	2 cups
5 mL	*cider vinegar*	1 tsp
Dash	*hot pepper sauce*	Dash

In large saucepan over high heat, combine squash, broccoli, tomato and 500 mL (2 cups) of the chicken stock; bring to boil. Cook for 7 to 10 minutes or until vegetables are tender. Let cool slightly.

In food processor or blender, process squash mixture in batches, until smooth.

In same saucepan over high heat, heat remaining 250 mL (1 cup) chicken stock until boiling. Add broccoli florets and cook for about 3 minutes or until tender. Add vinegar, hot pepper sauce and puréed squash mixture. Reheat and serve immediately.

Makes 4 servings

HIGH FIBRE

GOOD *Source of* CALCIUM

FOODLAND ONTARIO

FOOD CHOICE VALUE	*per serving*
Each Serving: 1/4 of recipe	
1/2	☑ *Protein Choice*
1	◨ *Fruits & Vegetables Choice*
1	➕ *Extra*
14 g	*Carbohydrate*
7 g	*Protein*
1 g	*Total Fat*
374	*kilojoules (89 Calories)*

Fundy Bay Clam Chowder

Accompany this hearty soup with Herb Scones or fresh crusty bread.

1 kg	*boneless pork shoulder, cut into 1 cm (1/2 inch) cubes*	*2 lb*
25 mL	*vegetable oil*	*2 tbsp*
250 mL	*chopped onions*	*1 cup*
1	*small sweet green pepper, cubed*	*1*
1	*clove garlic, minced*	*1*
1	*can (796 mL/28 oz) tomatoes*	*1*
250 mL	*chicken stock*	*1 cup*
50 mL	*tomato paste*	*1/4 cup*
2 mL	*dried thyme*	*1/2 tsp*
Pinch	*cayenne pepper*	*Pinch*
1	*bay leaf*	*1*
1	*can (142 g/5 oz) clams (with liquid)*	*1*

MARINADE

250 mL	*white wine**	*1 cup*
15 mL	*paprika*	*1 tbsp*
2 mL	*salt*	*1/2 tsp*
3	*cloves garlic, minced*	*3*
1 mL	*pepper*	*1/4 tsp*
1	*bay leaf*	*1*

GARNISH

15 mL	*grated lemon rind*	*1 tbsp*
50 mL	*minced fresh parsley*	*1/4 cup*

Marinade: In large bowl, combine wine, paprika, salt, garlic, pepper and bay leaf; add pork and marinate in refrigerator for at least 5 hours or overnight. Drain pork well, reserving marinade.

In large heavy pan, heat oil; brown pork. Add onions, green pepper and garlic; sauté until softened. Add tomatoes, chicken stock, tomato paste, thyme, cayenne, bay leaf and reserved marinade. Simmer until meat is tender, 30 to 40 minutes.

Add clams and additional chicken stock if desired. Remove bay leaf. Taste and adjust seasonings. Garnish with lemon rind and parsley.

Makes 6 to 8 servings.

Reheat in the Microwave for lunch the next day.

Serves well with a variety of Main Meal Seafood recipes. See recipes starting on page 175.

**Ask your dietitian or doctor about the use of alcohol.*

FOOD CHOICE VALUE *per serving*

Each Serving: 1/8 of recipe

3	☑ *Protein Choices*
1	◨ *Fruits & Vegetables Choice*
1	▲ *Fats & Oils Choice*

13 g	*Carbohydrate*
20 g	*Protein*
14 g	*Total Fat*
1071	*kilojoules (255 Calories)*

Egg Drop Soup

Use your left-over chicken to make the broth and bring a taste of the Orient home to your kitchen. Try a naturally brewed soy sauce to give the soup a more delicate oriental flavor.

1 L	*chicken broth*	*4 cups*
25 mL	*soy sauce*	*2 tbsp*
1	*green onion, thinly sliced*	*1*
2	*eggs*	*2*

In 2 L (8-cup) microwaveable bowl, combine chicken broth and soy sauce. Microwave at High (100% power) 10 to 12 minutes or until boiling. Stir in green onion.

Beat eggs lightly; slowly pour eggs in a thin stream into broth, stirring gently. Serve immediately.

Makes 4 servings.

MICROWAVEABLE

If concerned about sodium intake, substitute low-sodium soy sauce.

FOOD CHOICE VALUE *per serving*

Each Serving : 1/4 of recipe

1 1/2 ☑ *Protein Choices*

2 g	*Carbohydrate*
9 g	*Protein*
4 g	*Total Fat*
345	*kilojoules (83 Calories)*

Cauliflower Lentil Soup

Lentils are a tasty, low-fat way to add fibre and protein to your diet. Here they combine with lots of cauliflower to make a mouth-watering make-ahead dish.

250 mL	*dried brown or red lentils, rinsed*	*1 cup*
1	*medium onion, finely chopped*	*1*
1	*stalk celery, finely chopped*	*1*
1	*medium carrot, diced*	*1*
1	*clove garlic, minced*	*1*
1	*bay leaf*	*1*
750 mL	*beef stock*	*3 cups*
500 mL	*coarsely chopped cauliflower*	*2 cups*
5 mL	*cider vinegar*	*1 tsp*
	Salt and pepper	

In large saucepan over high heat, combine lentils, onion, celery, carrot, garlic, bay leaf and stock; bring to boil. Reduce heat and simmer for about 7 minutes or until lentils are nearly tender.

Add cauliflower and vinegar; cook for 5 minutes or until lentils and cauliflower are tender. Remove bay leaf. Season to taste with salt and pepper.

Makes 4 servings.

FOOD CHOICE VALUE *per serving*

Each Serving: 1/4 of recipe

1	⊘ *Protein Choice*
1	☐ *Starchy Choice*
1	◨ *Fruits & Vegetables Choice*
1	➕ *Extra*

27 g	Carbohydrate
13 g	Protein
0 g	Total Fat
664	kilojoules (158 Calories)

FOODLAND ONTARIO

Mushroom Tomato Pasta Soup

When you long to savor something soothing, something homemade, nothing does the trick like a hearty meal – soup. Just serve with crusty bread, salad and fresh fruit for dessert. A tasty alternative to a full course dinner.

25 mL	butter or soft margarine	2 tbsp
1	medium onion, chopped	1
500 mL	sliced mushrooms	2 cups
1	can (540 mL / 19 oz)* stewed tomatoes	1
1	can (284 mL / 10 oz) chicken broth plus 1 can water	1
2 mL	crumbled dried tarragon or basil leaves	1/2 tsp
175 mL	baby pasta shells, macaroni or orzo	3/4 cup
500 mL	packed fresh spinach, torn into bite-size pieces	2 cups
300 mL	shredded Swiss cheese	1 1/4 cups

In large saucepan, melt butter over medium-high heat; sauté onion and mushrooms for 2 minutes.

Add tomatoes, chicken broth and water and tarragon; bring to boil. Stir in pasta reduce heat and simmer, uncovered, for 10 minutes or until pasta is tender, stirring occasionally.

Stir in spinach; heat for 1 minute or just until wilted. Serve immediately in bowls; sprinkle with cheese.

Makes 4 servings, each 525 mL/17.5 oz.

Any small shape pasta could be substituted for shells. Use hot water to reduce time for soup to come to a boil. This soup should be served when prepared, or pasta will absorb all the broth and spinach will be limp.

*Recipe has been developed for use with 19 oz or 28 oz can sizes. Nutritional analysis based on 19 oz size only.

FOOD CHOICE VALUE *per serving*

Each Serving: 1/4 recipe

2	Protein Choices
1 1/2	Starchy Choices
1	Fruits & Vegetables Choice
2	Fats & Oils Choices
37 g	Carbohydrate
20 g	Protein
17 g	Total Fat
1545	kilojoules (368 Calories)

Cucumber Leek Soup

Enjoy the crunchy taste of garden fresh vegetables in this soup accented with dillweed and chopped parsley. It makes a light, nutritious and satisfying start to any meal.

2	cans (284 mL/10 oz) condensed chicken broth	2
125 mL	water	1/2 cup
1	large cucumber, peeled, seeded and sliced	1
1	large leek (white part only), sliced	1
25 mL	chopped fresh parsley	2 tbsp
2 mL	dried dillweed, crushed	1/2 tsp
Pinch	pepper	Pinch
50 mL	plain low-fat yogurt	1/4 cup

In 2 L (8-cup) microwaveable casserole, combine broth, water, cucumber and leek. Cover with lid; microwave at High (100% power) 8 minutes or until boiling.

With slotted spoon, transfer vegetables to blender or food processor. Add 125 mL (1/2 cup) of the broth mixture, parsley, dill and pepper; blend until smooth. Return mixture to broth. Cover and microwave at High 4 minutes or until hot and bubbling.

Ladle into bowls; top with yogurt.

Makes 4 servings.

FOOD CHOICE VALUE *per serving*

Each Serving: 1/4 of recipe

1 ☑ *Protein Choice*

1 ☐ *Fruits & Vegetables Choice*

9 g	Carbohydrate
8 g	Protein
2 g	Total Fat
349	kilojoules (83 Calories)

MINI MEALS
&
SALADS

	Microwave	Protein	Starchy	Fruits & Vegetables	Fats & Oils	Extra	Page
Tostada Turkey Salad *(Photo: p. 54)*		3	1 1/2			1	71
Chicken Rice Salad with Chutney Dressing	●	1 1/2	1	1 1/2	1		72
Thai Beef Salad *(Photo: p. 54)*		4		1 1/2			73
Tomato, Beef and Pasta Salad Olé		1 1/2	1		1 1/2		74
Grandma's Chicken Salad		2		1			75
Spiced Onion and Rare Beef		3 1/2		1 1/2	1		76
Wild Rice Salad			1/2	1/2	2		77
Warm Pork and Cabbage Salad		4		1	1		78
Pepper Steak Pasta Salad		3 1/2	1	1			79
Barley Salad with Shrimp & Scallops	●	1	1	1/2			80
Tomato Wild Rice Tabbouleh Salad			1/2	1/2	2	1	81
Mexican Stir-Fry Salad *(Photo on front cover.)*		4		1/2			82

The Food Choice Values on each recipe do not include accompanying foods which are suggested in many of the recipes and shown in some of the photographs.

PHOTO ON PAGE 54.

Tostada Turkey Salad

Get the most out of your left-over turkey with this popular Mexican main-dish salad with its provocative blend of vegetables, topped off with a spicy vinaigrette dressing. This recipe has been lightened, by having the tortillas baked to cracker-like crispness rather than being fried.

4	*flour tortillas*	4
1 L	*shredded lettuce*	4 cups
2	*medium tomatoes, coarsely chopped*	2
Half	*small red onion, sliced and separated in rings*	Half
250 g	*cooked turkey, cut in thin slivers*	1/2 lb
125 mL	*coarsely chopped watercress*	1/2 cup
2	*radishes, thinly sliced*	2

SPICY VINAIGRETTE DRESSING

20 mL	*vegetable oil*	4 tsp
25 mL	*red wine vinegar*	2 tbsp
25 mL	*water*	2 tbsp
2 mL	*dry mustard*	1/2 tsp
1	*clove garlic, minced*	1
Pinch	*crushed hot pepper flakes*	Pinch

Spicy Vinaigrette Dressing: In small bowl, whisk together oil, vinegar, water, mustard, garlic and hot pepper flakes. Set aside.

Arrange tortillas in single layer on large baking sheet. Bake in 220°C (425°F) oven until crisp and lightly browned, about 3 minutes.

Place hot tortillas on serving plates. Top with lettuce, tomatoes, onion and turkey. Garnish with watercress and radishes. Drizzle with dressing.

Makes 4 servings, each 260 g/9 oz.

FOOD CHOICE VALUE	*per serving*
Each Serving: 1/4 of recipe	
3	☑ *Protein Choices*
1 1/2	▫ *Starchy Choices*
1	▐▐ *Extra*

24 g	*Carbohydrate*
22 g	*Protein*
10 g	*Total Fat*
1150	*kilojoules (274 Calories)*

Chicken Rice Salad with Chutney Dressing

Great for a light summer dinner on a hot night. Looks attractive served on a bed of lettuce. Serve with fresh rolls and a chilled soup.

1	*can (284 mL/10 oz) condensed chicken broth*	*1*
75 mL	*chutney*	*1/3 cup*
15 mL	*mayonnaise*	*1 tbsp*
2 mL	*curry powder*	*1/2 tsp*
Pinch	*grated lime rind*	*Pinch*
2	*chicken breasts, skinned and boned*	*2*
50 mL	*water*	*1/4 cup*
175 mL	*long-grain rice*	*3/4 cup*
125 mL	*frozen peas, thawed*	*1/2 cup*
50 mL	*toasted chopped pecans*	*1/4 cup*
	Pecan halves	

In small bowl, combine 50 mL (1/4 cup) of the broth, chutney, mayonnaise, curry powder and lime rind. Set aside.

In 3 L (12-cup) microwaveable casserole, cover and microwave chicken at High (100% power) 4 minutes or until no longer pink inside, rearranging once during cooking. Remove from casserole; set aside.

In same casserole, combine remaining broth, water and rice. Cover and microwave at High 4 minutes or until bubbling. Microwave at Medium (50% power) 10 minutes. Stir in peas. Let stand, covered, 5 minutes or until liquid is absorbed.

Meanwhile, cut chicken into bite-size pieces. Add chicken, chopped pecans and dressing to rice mixture; toss to mix well. Cover; refrigerate until chilled, at least 4 hours. Garnish with pecan halves.

Makes 6 servings.

MICROWAVEABLE

You'll notice that microwave recipes often direct you to pierce or puncture foods with a fork or skewer. Without piercing, microwaves cause steam to build up in foods. The trapped steam may cause foods to explode. Some foods that must be pierced are: whole eggs, egg yolks, potatoes and other whole vegetables.

FOOD CHOICE VALUE *per serving*

Each Serving: 1/6 of recipe

1 1/2	☑	*Protein Choices*
1	☐	*Starchy Choice*
1 1/2	◪	*Fruits & Vegetables Choices*
1	▲	*Fats & Oils Choice*

29 g	*Carbohydrate*
15 g	*Protein*
8 g	*Total Fat*
1050	*kilojoules (250 Calories)*

Thai Beef Salad

PHOTO ON PAGE 54.

A little leftover roast beef is all you need to start preparing this imaginative dish with its hint of gingerroot. Double or triple the recipe next time you're asked to contribute to a pot-luck buffet. The cantaloupe perimeter makes for an attractive presentation.

2	*limes*	2
1	*piece (1 cm/1/2 inch) gingerroot, minced*	1
25 mL	*chopped fresh coriander or parsley*	2 tbsp
25 mL	*chopped fresh mint (or 7 mL/1 1/2 tsp dried)*	2 tbsp
15 mL	*peanut oil*	1 tbsp
15 mL	*water*	1 tbsp
2 mL	*sesame oil*	1/2 tsp
1 mL	*salt*	1/4 tsp
375 g	*cooked roast beef, cut into strips (750 mL/3 cups)*	3/4 lb
1	*small cantaloupe, sliced in thin wedges*	1
1	*small head romaine lettuce, shredded*	1
7 mL	*sesame seeds*	1 1/2 tsp
	Hot pepper flakes	

Cut 1 lime into wedges for garnish. Grate rind of remaining lime and squeeze enough juice to make 50 mL (1/4 cup), reserving any extra.

In bowl, combine lime juice, lime rind, ginger, coriander, mint, peanut oil, water, sesame oil and salt. Add roast beef strips and toss well.

Arrange sliced cantaloupe around edge of platter; mound lettuce in centre to form bed. Spoon roast beef mixture over lettuce. Sprinkle with any reserved lime juice. Garnish with lime wedges. Top with sesame seeds and sprinkling of hot pepper flakes.

Makes 4 servings.

FOOD CHOICE VALUE *per serving*

Each Serving: 1/4 of recipe

4 ☑ *Protein Choices*

1 1/2 ☐ *Fruits & Vegetables Choices*

14 g	Carbohydrate
30 g	Protein
13 g	Total Fat
1214	kilojoules (289 Calories)

Tomato, Beef and Pasta Salad Olé

This red, white and green salad contains flavors of sunny Mexico as well as the colors of the Mexican flag. Turn into a main course by adding cooked slivers of roast beef, pork or chicken. Extra hot peppers may be added when more "heat" is desired.

75 mL	*vegetable oil*	*1/3 cup*
125 mL	*chopped fresh parsley*	*1/2 cup*
50 mL	*chopped chives*	*3 tbsp*
1	*clove garlic, minced*	*1*
5 mL	*Worcestershire sauce*	*1 tsp*
5 mL	*salt*	*1 tsp*
2 mL	*hot pepper flakes*	*1/2 tsp*
1 mL	*pepper*	*1/4 tsp*
6	*medium tomatoes, chopped*	*6*
375 mL	*slivered cooked roast beef, pork or chicken*	*1 1/2 cups*
500 mL	*penne pasta*	*2 cups*

Combine oil, parsley, chives, garlic, Worcestershire sauce, salt, hot pepper flakes and pepper; pour over tomatoes in large bowl. Stir in cooked meat. Marinate in refrigerator for 1 hour.

Cook pasta according to package directions; drain and add to tomato mixture, stirring to mix well.

Makes 8 servings.

Spicy

FOOD CHOICE VALUE *per serving*

Each Serving: 1/8 of recipe

1 1/2 ☑ *Protein Choices*

1 ☐ *Starchy Choice*

1 1/2 ▲ *Fats & Oils Choices*

---

16 g *Carbohydrate*

14 g *Protein*

12 g *Total Fat*

949 *kilojoules (226 Calories)*

Grandma's Chicken Salad

Bright red tomatoes filled with caraway-flavored chicken, apples and cabbage slaw make this salad a treat for the eye as well as the tastebuds.

If necessary, you can cut a thin slice off the bottom of the tomato to make it stand upright.

500 mL	*diced cooked chicken*	2 cups
250 mL	*diced (unpeeled) red apple*	1 cup
500 mL	*slivered cabbage*	2 cups
50 mL	*light mayonnaise*	4 tbsp
45 mL	*minced fresh parsley*	3 tbsp
15 mL	*caraway seed*	1 tbsp
2 mL	*celery salt*	1/2 tsp
6	*large firm tomatoes*	6

In bowl, combine chicken, apple, cabbage, mayonnaise, parsley, caraway seeds and celery salt; refrigerate for at least 1 hour or until chilled.

Cut tops off tomatoes. Scoop out pulp and discard, leaving thick enough wall to remain firm. Fill with chicken mixture.

Makes 6 servings.

FOOD CHOICE VALUE *per serving*

Each Serving: 1/6 of recipe

2 ☑ *Protein Choices*

1 ◨ *Fruits & Vegetables Choice*

11 g	Carbohydrate
16 g	Protein
7 g	Total Fat
722	kilojoules (172 Calories)

Spiced Onion and Rare Beef

An unusual marriage of Japanese and French cuisine, this combines
onions and beef attractively and with a special piquancy.

50 mL	*vegetable oil*	*3 tbsp*
1	*medium onion, chopped*	*1*
1	*clove garlic, minced*	*1*
3	*medium onions, sliced in rings*	*3*
125 mL	*red wine vinegar*	*1/2 cup*
125 mL	*water*	*1/2 cup*
50 mL	*chili sauce*	*1/4 cup*
15 mL	*granulated sugar*	*1 tbsp*
2 mL	*hot pepper sauce*	*1/2 tsp*
1 mL	*dried basil*	*1/4 tsp*
1 mL	*dried thyme*	*1/4 tsp*
1	*bay leaf*	*1*
	Black peppercorns	
500 g	*flank steak, scored*	*1 lb*
	Salt and pepper	

In large skillet, heat oil over medium heat; sauté chopped onion
and garlic until tender, about 3 minutes. Add sliced onions, vinegar,
water, chili sauce, sugar, hot pepper sauce, basil, thyme, bay leaf
and a few peppercorns; bring to boil. Cook, stirring, for 5 minutes.
Cover and reduce heat to simmer; cook 5 minutes. Remove bay leaf.
Let cool and refrigerate until chilled.

On broiling pan, sprinkle steak with salt and pepper to taste. Broil 5
cm (2 inches) from heat for 3 to 4 minutes each side or until rare.
Remove to cutting board and cool.

With sharp knife, cut steak across the grain into thin slices.
Arrange on serving platter. Top with spiced onion mixture.

Makes 4 servings.

FOOD CHOICE VALUE	*per serving*
Each Serving: 1/4 of recipe	
3 1/2 ☑ *Protein Choices*	
1 1/2 ◨ *Fruits & Vegetables Choices*	
1 ▲ *Fats & Oils Choice*	

15 g	*Carbohydrate*
28 g	*Protein*
17 g	*Total Fat*
1440	*kilojoules (319 Calories)*

Prepare Ahead

Wild Rice Salad

This deliciously different salad idea is made ahead of time and marinated so each grain of rice is bursting with flavor. Serve in hollowed-out tomato halves for lunch or summer supper, or spoon into a pita for a packed lunch. Serves well at dinner instead of potatoes.

125 mL	*wild rice*	*1/2 cup*
375 mL	*boiling water*	*1 1/2 cups*
3	*stalks celery, diced*	*3*
2	*medium carrots, grated*	*2*
4	*green onions, thinly sliced*	*4*
75 mL	*vegetable oil*	*1/3 cup*
50 mL	*red wine vinegar*	*3 tbsp*
2 mL	*salt*	*1/2 tsp*
0.5 mL	*pepper*	*1/8 tsp*
1 mL	*dry mustard*	*1/4 tsp*
2 mL	*dried tarragon*	*1/2 tsp*
50 mL	*light mayonnaise*	*1/4 cup*

Quick soak wild rice. In saucepan, stir wild rice into 375 mL (1 1/2 cups) boiling water; simmer, covered, 20 minutes. Drain.

In bowl, combine celery, carrots and onions; add rice and toss to mix. In jar with tight-fitting lid, shake together oil, vinegar, salt, pepper, mustard and tarragon; pour over rice mixture and toss to mix well. Marinate, covered, in refrigerator 4 hours. At serving time, stir in mayonnaise.

Makes 8 servings.

FOOD CHOICE VALUE *per serving*

Each Serving: 125 mL (1/2 cup)

1/2 ☐ *Starchy Choice*

1/2 ◪ *Fruits & Vegetables Choice*

2 ▲ *Fats & Oils Choices*

---

10 g	*Carbohydrate*
2 g	*Protein*
11 g	*Total Fat*
617	*kilojoules (147 Calories)*

Warm Pork and Cabbage Salad

This recipe uses foods popular in traditional German cuisine and combines them in an updated style. The result is an attractively arranged salad with three types of cabbage and a warm apple-flavored dressing. Garnish with raw carrot sticks and fresh onion rings if desired.

500 mL	*shredded red cabbage*	*2 cups*
500 mL	*shredded green cabbage*	*2 cups*
500 mL	*shredded savoy cabbage*	*2 cups*
4	*slices bacon*	*4*
1	*medium onion, sliced*	*1*
500 g	*pork tenderloin, cut in 1 cm (1/4 inch) slices*	*1 lb*

DRESSING

50 mL	*apple juice*	*3 tbsp*
25 mL	*apple cider vinegar*	*2 tbsp*
15 mL	*Dijon mustard*	*1 tbsp*
2 mL	*dried thyme*	*1/2 tsp*
1 mL	*salt*	*1/4 tsp*
0.5 mL	*pepper*	*1/8 tsp*

Dressing: Combine apple juice, vinegar, mustard, thyme, salt and pepper; set aside.

Salad: Attractively arrange 125 mL (1/2 cup) of each cabbage on 4 serving plates.

In large skillet over medium-high heat, cook bacon until crisp. Remove from pan; let cool and crumble. To bacon drippings in pan, add onion and sauté 2 minutes; push to side of pan. Sauté pork for 4 minutes, browning on all sides. Stir in dressing; bring to boil.

Spoon pork and dressing over cabbage. Sprinkle with crumbled bacon. Serve immediately.

Makes 4 servings.

FOOD CHOICE VALUE *per serving*

Each Serving: 1/4 of recipe

4	☑ *Protein Choices*
1	◻ *Fruits & Vegetables Choice*
1	▲ *Fats & Oils Choice*

---

10 g	*Carbohydrate*
31 g	*Protein*
17 g	*Total Fat*
1315	*kilojoules (313 Calories)*

Pepper Steak Pasta Salad

Brimming with flavor, color and texture, this is a make-ahead meal to enjoy. For added variety, try using different shapes and colors of pasta, rice or egg noodles, broken into 10 cm (4 inch) pieces.

15 mL	*olive oil*	*1 tbsp*
15 mL	*red wine vinegar*	*1 tbsp*
15 mL	*beef stock*	*1 tbsp*
1 to 2	*cloves garlic, minced*	*1 to 2*
	Pepper	
750 g	*round or sirloin tip steak*	*1 1/2 lb*
500 mL	*rotini noodles*	*2 cups*
125 mL	*small cauliflower florets*	*1/2 cup*
125 mL	*small broccoli florets*	*1/2 cup*
2	*carrots, julienned*	*2*
Half	*each sweet red and green pepper, julienned*	*Half*
2	*green onions, thinly sliced*	*2*
250 mL	*light Italian or Caesar-style salad dressing*	*1 cup*
2 mL	*salt*	*1/2 tsp*
	Grated Parmesan cheese (optional)	

In shallow baking dish, combine oil, vinegar, beef stock, garlic, and pepper to taste. Pierce steak at regular intervals with fork; add to marinade and turn to coat. Cover and refrigerate to marinate for 8 hours or overnight, turning occasionally.

Remove steak from marinade. Broil for 4 to 5 minutes per side for medium-rare. Cut in very thin slices diagonally across the grain.

Meanwhile, cook pasta in boiling water until tender but still firm; drain and rinse in cold water. Blanch cauliflower, broccoli and carrots; cool immediately in ice water and pat dry.

In large bowl, combine steak, pasta, cauliflower, broccoli, carrots, red and green peppers, onions, salad dressing, salt, and pepper to taste. Let stand for 1 hour to blend flavors. Garnish with Parmesan cheese, if desired.

Makes 6 servings, each 200g/7 oz.

Prepare Ahead

To julienne, or cut vegetables into matchstick-size pieces, slice them lengthwise into about 3 mm (1/8-inch) thickness. Then, with cut side down, cut lengthwise into strips. Cut crosswise into 5 cm (2-inch) pieces.

GOOD Source of IRON

FOOD CHOICE VALUE *per serving*

Each Serving: 1/6 of recipe

3 1/2	☑	*Protein Choices*
1	☐	*Starchy Choice*
1	◪	*Fruits & Vegetables Choice*

27 g	*Carbohydrate*
27 g	*Protein*
9 g	*Total Fat*
1247	*kilojoules (297 Calories)*

Barley Salad with Shrimp and Scallops

Chilled, ready and waiting in the refrigerator, this is a tasty make-ahead salad for seafood lovers. For an attractive presentation, serve dinner table portions in large scallop shells.

1	*can (284 mL/10 oz) condensed chicken broth*	*1*
15 mL	*lemon juice*	*1 tbsp*
1	*small clove garlic, minced*	*1*
125 g	*medium shrimp, peeled and deveined*	*1/4 lb*
125 g	*bay scallops*	*1/4 lb*
5 mL	*Dijon-style mustard*	*1 tsp*
50 mL	*water*	*1/4 cup*
125 mL	*pearl barley*	*1/2 cup*
250 mL	*thinly sliced broccoli stalks*	*1 cup*
125 mL	*canned kernel corn, drained*	*1/2 cup*
50 mL	*sliced celery*	*1/4 cup*
15 mL	*chopped chives*	*1 tbsp*

MICROWAVEABLE

To remove food odors from the microwave oven, place a cut lemon in a custard cup. Microwave, uncovered, at High about 1 minute.

In 3 L (12-cup) microwaveable casserole, combine 50 mL (1/4 cup) of the broth, lemon juice and garlic. Stir in shrimp and scallops.

Cover with lid; microwave at High (100% power) 3 minutes or until shrimp are pink and scallops are opaque. Transfer shrimp mixture to small bowl; stir in mustard. Cover; set aside.

In same casserole, combine remaining broth, water and barley. Cover and microwave at High 5 minutes. Microwave at Medium (50% power) 20 minutes or until liquid is absorbed.

Add reserved shrimp mixture, broccoli, corn, celery and chives; toss to mix well. Cover; refrigerate until chilled, at least 4 hours.

Makes 5 servings.

FOOD CHOICE VALUE *per serving*

Each Serving: 1/5 of recipe

1	☑	*Protein Choice*
1	☐	*Starchy Choice*
1/2	◧	*Fruits & Vegetables Choice*

22 g	*Carbohydrate*
12 g	*Protein*
1 g	*Total Fat*
613	*kilojoules (146 Calories)*

Tomato Wild Rice Tabbouleh Salad

This Middle Eastern specialty is fresh tasting and nutritious.
The interesting flavor comes from a combination of mint and garlic
and the nutrition results from the wild rice and tomatoes.

For an impressive presentation, serve tabbouleh salad in hollowed out tomatoes.

125 mL	wild rice	1/2 cup
4	medium tomatoes	4
2	green onions, sliced	2
50 mL	chopped fresh mint (or 15 mL/1 tbsp dried)	1/4 cup

DRESSING

50 mL	vegetable oil	1/4 cup
25 mL	lemon juice	2 tbsp
1	large clove garlic, minced	1
2 mL	hot pepper sauce	1/2 tsp
2 mL	salt	1/2 tsp
0.5 mL	pepper	1/8 tsp
	Leaf lettuce	

Wash wild rice under cold running water; stir into saucepan of
375 mL (1 1/2 cups) boiling water. Simmer, covered, for 5 minutes.
Remove from heat and let soak in same water, covered, for 1 hour.
Drain. Stir wild rice into 375 mL (1 1/2 cups) boiling water; simmer
covered, 25 minutes. Drain and cool.

Cut tomatoes into 2.5 cm (1 inch) cubes; place in large bowl.
Add cooled wild rice, green onions and mint, stirring to mix.

Dressing: In jar with tight-fitting lid, shake together oil, lemon
juice, garlic, hot pepper sauce, salt and pepper until well blended.
Pour over salad. Stir, cover and chill for at least 1 hour. Serve in
lettuce-lined bowl.

Makes 6 servings.

FOOD CHOICE VALUE *per serving*

Each Serving: 1/6 of recipe

1/2	□ *Starchy Choice*
1/2	◪ *Fruits & Vegetables Choice*
2	▲ *Fats & Oils Choices*
1	✚ *Extra*

14 g	*Carbohydrate*
3 g	*Protein*
8 g	*Total Fat*
580	*kilojoules (138 Calories)*

FOODLAND ONTARIO

Mexican Stir-Fry Salad

Adjust the level of heat in this quick-and-easy stir-fry according
to the amount of jalapeño pepper.

500 g	*top round steak*	*1 lb*
25 mL	*vegetable oil*	*2 tbsp*
5 mL	*each ground cumin and dried oregano*	*1 tsp*
1	*clove garlic, minced*	*1*
1	*sweet red pepper, cut in thin strips*	*1*
1	*medium onion, cut in thin wedges*	*1*
1 to 2	*jalapeño peppers, slivered*	*1 to 2*
750 mL	*finely sliced romaine lettuce*	*3 cups*

Cut steak diagonally across the grain into thin strips. Combine oil,
cumin, oregano and garlic; reserve half. In large nonstick skillet, heat
remaining oil mixture over medium-high heat until hot. Add red
pepper, onion and jalapeño pepper; stir-fry 2 to 3 minutes or until
crisp-tender. Remove and reserve.

In same pan, stir-fry beef, in batches, in reserved oil mixture for
2 minutes. Return vegetables to pan and heat through. Serve over
lettuce.

Makes 4 servings, each 200g/7 oz.

PHOTO ON COVER..

When handling hot peppers,
be careful not to rub your eyes.
The volatile oil released from the
pepper can be very irritating.

FOOD CHOICE VALUE *per serving*

Each Serving: 1/4 of recipe

4 ☑ *Protein Choices*

1/2 ☐ *Fruits & Vegetables Choice*

4 g	*Carbohydrate*
27 g	*Protein*
10 g	*Total Fat*
899	*kilojoules (214 Calories)*

QUICK MEALS

	Microwave	Protein	Starchy	Fruits & Vegetables	Fats & Oils	Extra	Page
Sliced Apples and Chops (*Photo: p. 89*)	•	3 1/2		1 1/2			84
Tarragon Pork Tenderloin (*Photo: p. 89*)	•	4		1/2			85
Spicy Turkey Stir-Fry (*Photo: p. 89*)		3		1			86
Pita Fajita (*Photo: p. 88*)		2 1/2	1		1		91
Oriental Pork	•	3		1/2			92
Garden-Fresh Turkey Stir-Fry		2 1/2				1	93
Fruity Turkey Cutlets		4		1/2			94
Quick One-Dish Turkey Dinner	•	3 1/2	1	1/2			95
Pork Steak à L'Orange		4		1	1		96
Jiffy Pepper Steak		3			1/2		97
Egg Plant Parmesan	•	2	1	1 1/2	1 1/2		98
Speedy Steak Stroganoff		3 1/2		1/2			99
Quick Vegetable Mini-Omelettes		1/2			1		100
Stuffed Green Peppers	•	4	1/2	1		1	101
Cabbage Rolls	•	2 1/2	1/2	1	1/2		102

The Food Choice Values on each recipe do not include accompanying foods which are suggested in many of the recipes and shown in some of the photographs.

Sliced Apples and Chops

Here's a delicious new way to spice up this basic staple. Particularly nice during Autumn when apples are fresh and crisp. Serve with egg noodles and green or yellow beans.

2	*bone-in pork loin chops,*	2
	2 to 2.5 cm (3/4 to 1-inch) thick	
75 mL	*apple juice*	*1/3 cup*
2 mL	*cinnamon*	*1/2 tsp*
5 mL	*cornstarch*	*1 tsp*
1	*small cooking apple, cored and sliced*	*1*

Trim visible fat from pork chops. In microwaveable dish, arrange chops, with meaty portion toward outside of dish. Cover with waxed paper; microwave at Medium-Low (30% power) for 4 minutes. Turn chops over; microwave 4 minutes or until meat has just lost its pinkness. Remove and discard drippings; keep warm.

In microwaveable container, combine apple juice, cinnamon, cornstarch and apple. Cover and microwave at High (100% power) for 3 to 5 minutes or until apple slices are tender; stirring occasionally. Pour over pork chops; cover with waxed paper and microwave at Medium (70% power) for 1 minute.

Makes 2 servings.

PHOTO ON PAGE 89.

A microwave roasting rack or inverted microwaveable saucer should be used to raise meat from the juices. This elevation prevents stewing.

FOOD CHOICE VALUE *per serving*

Each Serving: 1 Pork Chop

3 1/2 ☑ *Protein Choices*

1 1/2 ◻ *Fruits & Vegetables Choices*

14 g	*Carbohydrate*
27 g	*Protein*
12 g	*Total Fat*
1150	*kilojoules (274 Calories)*

Tarragon Tenderloin for Two

Pork Tenderloin is one of the most tender and lean cuts of pork (4 grams fat per 90g/3 oz serving). Turn this quick meal into a romantic dinner for two by adding tender-crisp asparagus and crunchy wild rice.

PHOTO ON PAGE 89.

1 mL	browning sauce	1/4 tsp
2 mL	dry tarragon	1/2 tsp
250 g	pork tenderloin	1/2 lb
25 mL	chopped onion	2 tbsp
25 mL	chicken stock	2 tbsp
25 mL	white wine	2 tbsp
1 mL	salt	1/4 tsp
10	small mushrooms, cut in half	10
1	egg yolk	1
25 mL	whipping cream	2 tbsp

In microwaveable dish, brush browning sauce and half of the tarragon onto pork tenderloin. Cover and microwave at High (100% power) for 3 to 5 minutes. Remove, let stand covered, until meat thermometer registers 70° to 75° C (160° to 170° F).

In microwaveable bowl, microwave onion and stock at High for 1-1/2 minutes. Add wine, remaining tarragon, salt and mushrooms; microwave at High for 2 minutes. Combine egg yolk and cream; stir into mixture. Microwave at High for 20 seconds.

Slice tenderloin into 1 cm (1/2 inch) thick slices. Pour sauce over meat.

Makes 2 servings.

Leftover roast pork can be sliced thinly for sandwiches, cut into strips and added to your favorite stir-fry recipe. Or toss it in a salad for a one-dish meal!

If reheating pork slices, add moisture (water or gravy) and microwave at Medium (50% power) or Medium-High (70% power) until warm.

FOOD CHOICE VALUE *per serving*

Each Serving: 1/2 of recipe

4 ☑ *Protein Choices*

1/2 ☐ *Fruits & Vegetables Choice*

---

3 g   Carbohydrate

29 g   Protein

13 g   Total Fat

1063   kilojoules (253 Calories)

Spicy Turkey Stir-Fry

Enlighten your taste buds with this tingling taste treat. Serve over hot fluffy rice and garnish with an orange wedge and a spray of Italian parsley.

PHOTO ON PAGE 89.

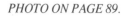

50 mL	*water*	*1/4 cup*
25 mL	*dry sherry*	*2 tbsp*
5 mL	*granulated sugar*	*1 tsp*
2 mL	*crushed hot pepper flakes*	*1/2 tsp*
300 g	*cubed cooked turkey*	*10 oz*
15 mL	*vegetable oil*	*1 tbsp*
1	*medium sweet red pepper, cubed*	*1*
200 g	*snow peas, trimmed*	*6 oz*
15 mL	*grated orange rind*	*1 tbsp*
15 mL	*minced gingerroot*	*1 tbsp*
10 mL	*cornstarch*	*2 tsp*
125 mL	*sliced water chestnuts*	*1/2 cup*
	Orange wedges	
	Parsley	

In bowl, combine water, sherry, sugar and hot pepper flakes. Add turkey and set aside.

In skillet, heat oil, add red pepper, snow peas, orange rind and ginger; stir fry 2 minutes.

Drain turkey, reserving marinade. Add cornstarch to marinade and stir to combine.

Add turkey, marinade and water chestnuts to skillet; cook, stirring constantly until thickened. Garnish with orange wedges and parsley.

Makes 4 servings, each 180g/6 1/2 oz.

FOOD CHOICE VALUE *per serving*

Each Serving: 1/4 of recipe

3	☑	*Protein Choices*
1	☐	*Fruits & Vegetables Choice*

11 g	*Carbohydrate*
24 g	*Protein*
7 g	*Total Fat*
903	*kilojoules (215 Calories)*

Cajun Pork Chops and Rice (p.139)   **87**

Pita Fajita (p.91)

Spicy Turkey Stir-Fry (p.86)

Tarragon Pork Tenderloin (p.85)

Sliced Apples and Chops (p.84)

89

Meatloaf Italiano (p.113)

Rice Primavera (p.104)

Pita Fajita

PHOTO ON PAGE 88.

Hot beef strips, zippy spices and refried beans combine to make this pita a pocketful of flavor that is filled with vitamins.

15 mL	vegetable oil	1 tbsp
2	cloves garlic, minced	2
125 mL	chopped onion	1/2 cup
125 mL	refried beans	1/2 cup
5 mL	ground cumin	1 tsp
2 mL	caraway seeds	1/2 tsp
125 g	flank or sirloin steak, cut in thin strips	1/4 lb
	Salt and pepper	
1	tomato, chopped	1
1	pita bread * (20 cm/8 inch)	1
125 mL	shredded Cheddar cheese	1/2 cup

* or 1 Flour Fajita shell (20 cm/8 inch)

In skillet, heat oil; cook garlic and onion, stirring, for 1 minute.

Add refried beans, cumin and caraway; cook, stirring, for 1 minute. Add steak strips; stir-fry just until beef loses pink color. Season with salt and pepper to taste. Remove from heat; add chopped tomato.

Cut pita in half and pull to open pockets. Divide filling between pockets. Top with cheese.

Makes 4 servings, each 1/4 of filled pita (5cm/2 inches).

FOOD CHOICE VALUE *per serving*

Each Serving: 1/4 of pita

2 1/2	☑ *Protein Choices*
1	☐ *Starchy Choice*
1	▲ *Fats & Oils Choice*

19 g	Carbohydrate
20 g	Protein
13 g	Total Fat
1166	kilojoules *(278 Calories)*

Oriental Pork

Tender morsels of pork marinated in sesame oil, ginger and soy sauce provides and aromatic taste of the Orient. Serve over a bed of fluffy rice. Serve with chop sticks on bamboo place mats.

5 mL	*sesame oil*	*1 tsp*
5 mL	*vegetable oil*	*1 tsp*
5 mL	*grated gingerroot*	*1 tsp*
15 mL	*soy sauce*	*1 tbsp*
15 mL	*dry sherry*	*1 tbsp*
1	*clove garlic, minced*	*1*
500 g	*boneless pork, cut in 5 cm x 1 mm (2- x 1/4-inch) strips*	*1 lb*
1	*can (284 mL/10 oz) condensed beef broth*	*1*
25 mL	*cornstarch*	*2 tbsp*
250 mL	*snow peas, trimmed*	*1 cup*
1	*sweet red pepper, cut in strips*	*1*
250 mL	*sliced fresh mushrooms*	*1 cup*

In 3 L (12-cup) microwaveable casserole, combine oils, ginger, soy sauce, sherry and garlic. Add pork; toss to coat. Cover with lid; refrigerate 1 hour.

Microwave, covered, at High (100% power) 5 minutes or until pork is no longer pink, stirring once during cooking.

In small bowl, combine broth and cornstarch; stir into pork mixture. Stir in peas, red pepper and mushrooms. Cover; microwave at High 7 minutes or until hot and bubbling, stirring three times during cooking.

Makes 5 servings.

MICROWAVEABLE

Because microwave ovens heat unevenly, you should stir the dish occasionally to redistribute the meat. Cook pork covered with either a tight-fitting lid or vented plastic wrap. The cover traps the cooking steam, which helps to distribute heat more evenly in the dish.

FOOD CHOICE VALUE *per serving*

Each Serving: 1/5 of recipe

3	✓	*Protein Choices*
1/2	◼	*Fruits & Vegetables Choice*

7 g	*Carbohydrate*
20 g	*Protein*
10 g	*Total Fat*
840	*kilojoules (200 Calories)*

Garden-Fresh Turkey Stir-Fry

Lean, nutritious and a snap to make. Turkey Stir-Fry has become very popular in recent years...and now turkey has better availability in grocery stores. Slice turkey and vegetables ahead of time, so this wholesome and delicious meal will ready in minutes.

2 mL	*each salt, pepper, garlic powder and paprika*	*1/2 tsp*
500 g	*turkey breast, cut in 1 cm (1/2 inch) strips*	*1 lb*
50 mL	*vegetable oil*	*3 tbsp*
1	*each sweet yellow and green peppers, thinly sliced*	*1*
250 mL	*snow peas*	*1 cup*
2 mL	*Italian seasoning*	*1/2 tsp*
8 to 10	*cherry tomatoes*	*8 to 10*

In plastic bag, combine salt, pepper, garlic powder and paprika. Add turkey strips and shake to coat with seasonings.

In skillet or wok, heat 25 mL (2 tbsp) oil; stir-fry turkey 3 to 4 minutes or until no longer pink inside. Remove from skillet; keep warm.

Add remaining oil, yellow and green peppers and snow peas; stir-fry 1 minute.

Sprinkle with Italian seasoning; reduce heat and cook 2 minutes until vegetables are tender-crisp. Add turkey and tomatoes; heat 2 minutes longer until warmed through.

Makes 6 servings, each 112 g/4 oz..

Prepare Ahead

FOOD CHOICE VALUE *per serving*

Each Serving: 1/6 of recipe

2 1/2 ◪ *Protein Choices*

1 ➕ *Extra*

---

4 g	*Carbohydrate*
19 g	*Protein*
1 g	*Total Fat*
424	*kilojoules (101 Calories)*

Fruity Turkey Cutlets

Tangy, tasty and ready in minutes, these flavorful cutlets are elegant enough for a special meal – without any of the stress.

625 g	*skinless boneless turkey breast*	*1-1/4 lb*
45 mL	*butter or soft margarine*	*3 tbsp*
15 mL	*finely chopped green onion*	*1 tbsp*
	Juice of 1 orange	
50 mL	*cranberry juice*	*1/4 cup*
2 mL	*dried thyme*	*1/2 tsp*
	Salt and pepper	

Slice turkey breast into cutlets 8 mm (1/3-inch) thick.

In large skillet, melt butter; add turkey and sauté over medium heat about 3 minutes per side. Stir in green onion, orange juice, cranberry juice, thyme, and salt and pepper to taste; bring to boil. Reduce heat, cover and simmer 5 minutes or until turkey feels springy and is no longer pink inside. Remove turkey to warm plate.

Boil pan juices, uncovered, 3 to 4 minutes until thickened and reduced to 125 mL (1/2 cup). Pour sauce over turkey.

Makes 4 servings, each 140 g/5 oz.

FOOD CHOICE VALUE *per serving*

Each Serving: 1/4 of recipe

4	*Protein Choices*
1/2	*Fruits & Vegetables Choice*

4 g	*Carbohydrate*
30 g	*Protein*
10 g	*Total Fat*
940	*kilojoules (225 Calories)*

Quick One-Dish Turkey Dinner

Excellent tomato flavor highlights this easy-to-fix family favorite. You can substitute canned corn for frozen if you wish.

15 mL	*all-purpose flour*	1 tbsp
1 mL	*each salt and dried thyme*	1/4 tsp
0.5 mL	*cayenne pepper*	1/8 tsp
125 mL	*chili sauce*	1/2 cup
1	*can (540 mL / 19 oz) tomatoes*	1
375 mL	*frozen corn*	1 1/2 cups
500 g	*turkey fillets, cut in 4*	1 lb
1	*sweet green pepper, chopped*	1

Conventional method: In large skillet, combine flour, salt, thyme and cayenne pepper. Stir in chili sauce, tomatoes and corn; mix well. Arrange turkey pieces in skillet; spoon tomato mixture over turkey.

Cover and simmer 18 to 20 minutes or until turkey is no longer pink inside. Stir in green pepper. Cover and simmer 3 to 5 minutes longer or until pepper is tender-crisp.

Microwave method: In 3 L (9- x 13-inch) microwaveable dish, combine flour, salt, thyme and cayenne pepper. Stir in chili sauce and tomatoes; mix well. Arrange turkey pieces in casserole, spoon tomato mixture over turkey.

Cover and microwave at High (100% power) for 5 minutes. Stir in corn. Cover and microwave at High for 8 to 10 minutes or until turkey is no longer pink inside, stirring once halfway through cooking. Stir in green pepper; cover and microwave at High for 1 to 2 minutes or until green pepper is tender-crisp.

Makes 5 servings.

You can make your own turkey fillets by slicing 625 g (1-1/4 lb) skinless, boneless turkey breast into 4 cutlets.

FOOD CHOICE VALUE *per serving*

Each Serving: 1/5 of recipe

3 1/2	☑	*Protein Choices*
1	☐	*Starchy Choice*
1/2	◪	*Fruits & Vegetables Choice*

---

25 g	*Carbohydrate*
27 g	*Protein*
0 g	*Total Fat*
882	*kilojoules (210 Calories)*

Pork Steak à L'Orange

This meal makes for an easy and delicious candle-light-and-wine dinner for two. Serve with slices of zucchini, carrots, fluffy white rice, and a healthy dollop of romance.

2	*boneless pork steaks or chops, at least 2.5 cm (1-inch) thick*	2
	Salt and pepper	
15 mL	*butter or soft margarine*	1 tbsp
5 mL	*finely chopped shallots*	1 tsp
1	*clove garlic, finely chopped*	1
125 mL	*orange juice*	1/2 cup
15 mL	*orange-flavored liqueur*	1 tbsp
15 mL	*grated orange rind*	1 tbsp
5 mL	*teriyaki sauce*	1 tsp

Trim fat from pork; season with salt and pepper to taste

In heavy skillet, heat butter; cook pork until no longer pink inside and juices run clear, being careful not to overcook. Remove from skillet and keep warm.

Add shallots and garlic to skillet; and sauté until softened. Add orange juice, liqueur, orange rind and teriyaki sauce; cook over medium-low heat until reduced to half. Pour over pork.

Makes 2 servings.

FOOD CHOICE VALUE *per serving*

Each Serving: 1 steak/chop

4	▨ *Protein Choices*
1	◩ *Fruits & Vegetables Choice*
1	▲ *Fats & Oils Choice*

14 g	*Carbohydrate*
28 g	*Protein*
10 g	*Total Fat*
1100	*kilojoules (262 Calories)*

Jiffy Pepper Steak

Enliven an ordinary, economical cut of steak with this recipe that takes just minutes to prepare. When not overcooked, its very tender. Also good cold in sandwiches or as part of a salad plate.

500 g	*inside round steak, 1 cm (1/2 inch) thick*	*1 lb*
5 mL	*pepper*	*1 tsp*
50 mL	*butter or soft margarine*	*3 tbsp*
15 mL	*Worcestershire sauce*	*1 tbsp*
15 mL	*lemon juice*	*1 tbsp*
1 mL	*celery salt*	*1/4 tsp*
Half	*clove garlic, minced*	*Half*

Cut steak into serving-size pieces. Sprinkle steak with pepper and rub into meat with heel of your hand.

In small saucepan, melt butter; add Worcestershire sauce, lemon juice, celery salt and garlic. Brush sauce on steaks and fast-fry over high heat 5 minutes or until desired doneness. Do not overcook. Serve immediately topped with remaining sauce.

Makes 4 servings, each 85 g/3 oz..

GOOD
Source of
IRON

FOOD CHOICE VALUE *per serving*

Each Serving: 1/4 of recipe

3	☑ *Protein Choices*	
1/2	▲ *Fats & Oils Choice*	

---

1 g	*Carbohydrate*
23 g	*Protein*
12 g	*Total Fat*
857	*kilojoules (204 Calories)*

Eggplant Parmesan

This microwave method helps you avoid extra calories.
Most conventional eggplant recipes require oil for frying or
broiling, but you don't need any here.

1	*egg*	*1*
25 mL	*milk*	*2 tbsp*
250 mL	*Italian-seasoned fine dry bread crumbs*	*1 cup*
1	*medium eggplant, peeled and cut into 1 mm (1/4-inch) slices*	*1*
425 mL	*spaghetti sauce*	*1 3/4 cups*
500 mL	*shredded low-fat mozzarella cheese*	*2 cups*
25 mL	*grated Parmesan cheese*	*2 tbsp*

In pie plate, beat egg and milk. Place crumbs in another pie plate.
Dip eggplant slices into egg mixture, then into crumbs to coat well.

Arrange half of the eggplant on 25 cm (10-inch) microwaveable
plate lined with paper towels. Microwave, uncovered, at High
(100% power) 4 minutes or until tender, rearranging slices once
during cooking. Repeat with remaining eggplant.

Spread 50 mL (1/4 cup) of the spaghetti sauce in 2 L (8-inch) square
microwaveable baking dish. Layer half of the eggplant, half of the
mozzarella and half of the remaining spaghetti sauce in dish; repeat
layers. Sprinkle with Parmesan cheese.

Cover with vented plastic wrap; microwave at High 4 minutes or
until hot. Rotate dish. Reduce to Medium (50% power). Microwave,
covered, 10 minutes or until hot and bubbling, rotating dish once
during cooking. Let stand, covered, 5 minutes.

Makes 6 servings.

FOOD CHOICE VALUE	*per serving*	
Each Serving: 1/6 of recipe		
2	☑	*Protein Choices*
1	☐	*Starchy Choice*
1 1/2	◪	*Fruits & Vegetables Choices*
1 1/2	◤	*Fats & Oils Choices*
31 g		*Carbohydrate*
17 g		*Protein*
13 g		*Total Fat*
1263		*kilojoules (301 Calories)*

Speedy Steak Stroganoff

Yogurt is a light alternative to the traditional sour cream in this dish.
Serve with hot cooked egg noodles or a rice pilaf.

500 g	*round or sirloin tip steak, cut in thin strips*	*1 lb*
125 mL	*beef broth*	*1/2 cup*
250 mL	*sliced fresh mushrooms*	*1 cup*
10 mL	*all-purpose flour*	*2 tsp*
5 mL	*onion powder*	*1 tsp*
75 mL	*plain low-fat yogurt*	*1/3 cup*
15 mL	*sherry or sweet white wine*	*1 tbsp*
	Salt and pepper	
	Minced fresh parsley	

In nonstick skillet over medium-high heat, brown beef, stirring often.
Add broth and mushrooms; cook 3 minutes.

Stir flour and onion powder into yogurt until smooth; add sherry.
Stir into beef mixture; cook, stirring constantly, until thickened.
Season with salt and pepper to taste. Sprinkle with parsley
to garnish.

Makes 4 servings, each 140g /5 oz.

FOOD CHOICE VALUE *per serving*

Each Serving: 1/4 of recipe

3 1/2 ☑ *Protein Choices*

1/2 ◨ *Fruits & Vegetables Choice*

4 g	*Carbohydrate*
25 g	*Protein*
5 g	*Total Fat*
689	*kilojoules (164 Calories)*

Quick Vegetable Mini-Omelettes

These light and colorful mini-omelettes make a satisfying quick meal the kids will love. For added fun, let the kids try eating them with chop sticks.

6	*eggs*	*6*
2	*cans (each 398 mL / 14 oz) cut green or wax beans, drained and coarsely chopped*	*2*
1	*small onion, grated*	*1*
15 mL	*minced gingerroot (or 2 mL / 1/2 tsp ground ginger)*	*1 tbsp*
Pinch	*each salt and pepper*	*Pinch*
25 mL	*vegetable oil*	*2 tbsp*
	Soy sauce	

In medium bowl, beat eggs. Stir in beans, onion, ginger, salt and pepper.

Heat lightly greased skilled over medium-high heat. Spoon egg mixture in 50 mL (1/4 cup) portions into skillet, shaping with spatula to form thin patties. Cook in batches, adding more oil if necessary, for 2 minutes per side or until golden brown and set. Serve with soy sauce.

Makes about 12 patties.

Ground Ginger is very versatile and excellent in combination with other spices. Use in sauces, soups, oriental dishes, all red meats, most vegetables. Ground Ginger may be substituted for Whole Ginger in most recipes: 1 tsp Ground Ginger is about the same as 10 pieces whole ginger (the size of shelled peanuts).

FOOD CHOICE VALUE *per serving*

Each Serving: 1 Omelette Pattie

1/2 ☑ *Protein Choice*

1 ▲ *Fats & Oils Choice*

2 g	*Carbohydrate*
4 g	*Protein*
5 g	*Total Fat*
281	*kilojoules (67 Calories)*

Stuffed Green Peppers

This gratifying meal of green peppers stuffed with ground turkey and rice, is easier than ever when prepared in the microwave. An excellent source of both Iron and Calcium. For a little sweeter taste, try using Red or Yellow peppers instead of Green.

500 g	*ground turkey*	*1 lb*
125 mL	*instant rice*	*1/2 cup*
125 mL	*finely chopped carrot*	*1/2 cup*
1	*small onion, finely chopped*	*1*
50 mL	*finely chopped fresh parsley*	*3 tbsp*
1	*clove garlic, minced*	*1*
1	*can (213 mL / 7-1/2 oz) tomato sauce*	*1*
2	*large sweet green peppers (or 4 small)*	*2*
125 mL	*shredded Cheddar cheese*	*1/2 cup*

In bowl, combine turkey, rice, carrot, onion, parsley, garlic and tomato sauce; mix well.

Cut peppers in half lengthwise; discard seeds and membranes. Spoon turkey mixture evenly into pepper shells.

Place stuffed peppers in microwaveable dish to fit snugly. Cover; and microwave at High (100% power) 12 to 15 minutes, rotating dish halfway through cooking. Sprinkle with cheese. Let stand 5 minutes before serving.

Makes 4 servings.

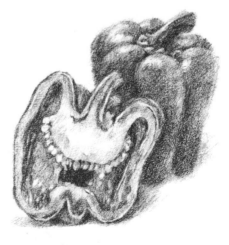

If you don't have any instant rice on hand, substitute 250 mL (1 cup) cooked rice.

EXCELLENT
Source of
IRON

EXCELLENT
Source of
CALCIUM

FOOD CHOICE VALUE *per serving*

Each Serving: 1/4 of recipe

4	⊘	*Protein Choices*
1/2	☐	*Starchy Choice*
1	◩	*Fruits & Vegetables Choice*
1	⊞	*Extra*

23 g	*Carbohydrate*
31 g	*Protein*
12 g	*Total Fat*
1351	*kilojoules* (322 Calories)

Cabbage Rolls

Bring back the aroma and taste of a european country kitchen, with this comforting and familiar fare that has never been so quick and easy.

6	*cabbage leaves*	*6*
125 mL	*water*	*1/2 cup*
500 g	*ground lean beef or pork*	*1 lb*
250 mL	*cooked rice*	*1 cup*
125 mL	*chopped onion*	*1/2 cup*
1	*egg*	*1*
15 mL	*Worcestershire sauce*	*1 tbsp*
Pinch	*pepper*	*Pinch*
1	*can (284 mL/10 oz) condensed tomato soup*	*1*
10 mL	*vinegar*	*2 tsp*

Arrange cabbage leaves in 3 L (12-cup) microwaveable casserole; add water. Cover with lid; microwave at High (100% power) 6 minutes or until soft, rotating dish once during cooking. Drain and set aside.

In medium bowl, thoroughly mix beef, rice, onion, egg, Worcestershire, pepper and 25 mL (2 tbsp) of the soup.

Lay drained cabbage leaves on counter. Spoon about 125 mL (1/2 cup) of the meat mixture onto each leaf. Fold in sides and roll up to form bundles; secure with wooden toothpicks if necessary. Arrange in same casserole.

In small bowl, combine remaining soup and vinegar; spoon over cabbage rolls. Cover and microwave at High 15 minutes or until meat is no longer pink, rotating dish once during cooking. Let stand, covered, 5 minutes.

Makes 6 servings.

FOOD CHOICE VALUE *per serving*

Each Serving: 1 cabbage roll

2 1/2	☑	*Protein Choices*
1/2	☐	*Starchy Choice*
1	◪	*Fruits & Vegetables Choice*
1/2	▲	*Fats & Oils Choice*

17 g	*Carbohydrate*
20 g	*Protein*
10 g	*Total Fat*
1008	*kilojoules (240 Calories)*

SIDE DISHES

VEGGIES

	Microwave	Protein	Starchy	Fruits & Vegetables	Fats & Oils	Page
Rice Primavera *(Photo: p. 90)*			1 1/2	1 1/2		104
Simple Corn and Carrot Sauté			1		1/2	105
Cajun Cabbage				1 1/2		106
Broccoli Sesame Stir-Fry		1/2		1/2	1	107
Green Beans Provencal				1/2	1/2	108
Fresh Vegetable Ring	•	1/2		1		109
Marinated Vegetables	•			1	1/2	110

The Food Choice Values on each recipe do not include accompanying foods which are suggested in many of the recipes and shown in some of the photographs.

Rice Primavera

Bright with colour and packed with freshness. This side dish compliments any main meal with it's multitude of vegetables. Particularly nice during late summer when vegetables are vine ripened and plentiful.

PHOTO ON PAGE 90.

50 mL	*butter*	*1/4 cup*
1 mL	*crushed dried oregano*	*1/4 tsp*
1 mL	*crushed dried basil*	*1/4 tsp*
1 mL	*garlic powder*	*1/4 tsp*
50 mL	*chopped onion*	*1/4 cup*
375 mL	*sliced zucchini*	*1 1/2 cups*
250 mL	*sliced mushrooms*	*1 cup*
250 mL	*kernel corn (fresh or frozen)*	*1 cup*
500 mL	*cooked rice*	*2 cups*
250 mL	*diced seeded tomatoes*	*1 cup*
	Salt and pepper	

In large frypan, melt butter; stir in oregano, basil and garlic powder. Add onion; sauté 2 to 3 minutes or until softened.

Add zucchini, mushrooms and corn. Cook, stirring, over medium heat until vegetables are tender and any liquid has evaporated.

Add rice and tomatoes. Cook until heated through. Season with salt and pepper to taste.

Makes about 6 servings, each 170g/6 oz.

FOOD CHOICE VALUE *per serving*

Each Serving: 1/6 of recipe

1 1/2 ☐ *Starchy Choices*

1 1/2 ◨ *Fruits & Vegetables Choices*

24 g	*Carbohydrate*
3 g	*Protein*
8 g	*Total Fat*
730	*kilojoules (174 Calories)*

Simple Corn and Carrot Sauté

Thyme and fresh parsley accented with a hint of lemon juice turn this simple concoction into a fresh-tasting side dish perfect for any occasion.

Thyme is used to season meat, poultry and fish. Excellent in tomato or cheese dishes. Combine Thyme with melted butter or soft margarine and serve over vegetables or broiled seafood.

15 mL	*butter or soft margarine*	*1 tbsp*
2	*carrots, grated*	*2*
Half	*small onion, finely chopped*	*Half*
1 mL	*dried thyme*	*1/4 tsp*
1	*can (341 mL/12 oz) kernel corn, drained*	*1*
7 mL	*lemon juice*	*1 1/2 tsp*
25 mL	*chopped fresh parsley*	*2 tbsp*
	(or 1 tbsp/15 mL dried), optional	
	Salt and pepper	

In skillet, melt butter over medium heat. Add carrots, onion and thyme; cook, stirring, for 4 minutes or until vegetables are softened.

Add corn; cook, stirring, 3 minutes longer or until heated through. Stir in lemon juice, parsley (if desired) and salt and pepper to taste.

Makes 4 servings.

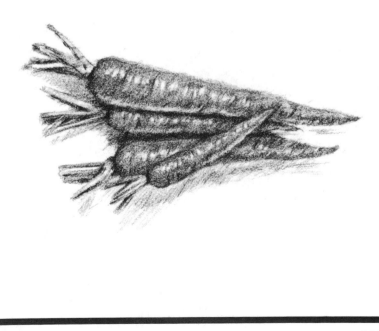

FOOD CHOICE VALUE *per serving*

Each Serving: 1/4 of recipe

1	☐ *Starchy Choice*
1/2	▲ *Fats & Oils Choice*

15 g	*Carbohydrate*
2 g	*Protein*
3 g	*Total Fat*
400	*kilojoules (95 Calories)*

Cajun Cabbage

This spicy Creole-style staple will perk up your taste buds with down-home New Orleans goodness. Serve with sausages or chops for a complete meal.

1 L	*coarsely shredded cabbage*	*4 cups*
1	*small onion, chopped*	*1*
1	*can (540 mL/19 oz) tomatoes*	*1*
1	*clove garlic, minced*	*1*
2 mL	*salt*	*1/2 tsp*
1 mL	*dried oregano*	*1/4 tsp*
1 mL	*pepper*	*1/4 tsp*
1 mL	*hot pepper sauce*	*1/4 tsp*
125 mL	*frozen kernel corn*	*1/2 cup*
125 mL	*frozen cut green beans*	*1/2 cup*

In large pot combine cabbage, onion, tomatoes, garlic, salt, oregano, pepper and hot pepper sauce. Cover and cook over medium low heat for 20 minutes or until cabbage is tender, stirring occasionally.

Add corn and beans; cover and cook for 5 minutes or until heated through.

Makes 4 servings.

FOOD CHOICE VALUE *per serving*

Each Serving: 1/4 of recipe

1 1/2 ◪ *Fruits & Vegetables Choices*

17 g	*Carbohydrate*
3 g	*Protein*
0 g	*Total Fat*
328	*kilojoules (78 Calories)*

Broccoli Sesame Stir-Fry

Gingeroot and broccoli turn this vegetarian stir-fry into a very nutritious and taste satisfying dish, accented with a delicate flavor of the orient. Try adding a touch of soy sauce and sesame seeds to a variety of vegetable dishes, not just Stir-Fry.

15 mL	sesame seeds	1 tbsp
1	bunch broccoli	1
15 mL	vegetable oil	1 tbsp
2 mL	grated gingerroot	1/2 tsp
15 mL	rice vinegar	1 tbsp
15 mL	soy sauce	1 tbsp

Toast sesame seeds in dry skillet over medium heat for 3 to 4 minutes or until lightly browned, shaking skillet frequently. Set aside.

Cut broccoli florets into bite-size pieces. Peel stems and slice thinly. In skillet or wok, heat oil over medium-high heat. Add broccoli and gingerroot; stir-fry for 3 minutes.

Stir in vinegar and soy sauce; cover and cook 1 minute longer or until broccoli is tender-crisp. Sprinkle with sesame seeds. Serve immediately.

Makes 4 servings.

Sesame Seeds can be used toasted or untoasted in much the way nuts are used. When toasted the flavor resembles that of toasted almonds. To toast, place on baking sheet in 350°F oven for 15 minutes or until lightly browned. Sprinkle Sesame Seeds on breads, casseroles, salads, vegetables, noodles.

FOOD CHOICE VALUE *per serving*

Each Serving: 1/4 of recipe

1/2	☑ *Protein Choice*
1/2	◨ *Fruits & Vegetables Choice*
1	▲ *Fats & Oils Choice*

7 g	*Carbohydrate*
4 g	*Protein*
5 g	*Total Fat*
357	*kilojoules* (85 Calories)

Green Beans Provençal

Now here's a simple Green Beans and Tomato side dish with a delicate blend of herbs. This also makes a snazzy breakfast variation when used as an omelette filling.

10 mL	*vegetable oil*	*2 tsp*
1	*small onion, finely chopped*	*1*
2	*cloves garlic, minced*	*2*
2 mL	*each dried thyme and basil*	*1/2 tsp*
1	*can (398 mL / 14 oz) tomatoes (undrained)*	*1*
2	*cans (each 398 mL / 14 oz) cut green beans, drained*	*2*
	Salt and pepper	
	Chopped fresh parsley (optional)	

In skillet, heat oil over medium heat; add onion and garlic. Cook for 3 minutes or until onion is softened. Stir in thyme and basil; cook 1 minute, stirring.

Break up tomatoes and add, with juice, to skillet. Increase heat to high; cook 3 to 4 minutes or until slightly thickened. Stir in beans, tossing to coat; cook until just heated through. Season with salt and pepper to taste. Garnish with chopped fresh parsley if desired.

Makes 6 servings.

Basil is sometimes called the "tomato herb" and may be used in most Tomato recipes. Basil blends well with other herbs in seasoning foods. Suggested amounts to use: -1/4 to 1/2 tsp in 2 cups green vegetables. -3/4 to 1 1/2 tsp for 1 1/2 lbs pork chops or roasts.

FOOD CHOICE VALUE *per serving*

Each Serving: 1/6 of recipe

1/2 ◪ ***Fruits & Vegetables Choice***
1/2 ▲ ***Fats & Oils Choice***

6 g	***Carbohydrate***
1 g	***Protein***
2 g	***Total Fat***
168	***kilojoules** (40 Calories)*

Fresh Vegetable Ring

This recipe demonstrates how the arrangement of food can compensate for differences in cooking time. Dense vegetables such as cauliflower, which take longer to cook than soft vegetables, are placed around the edge of the platter where they absorb more microwave energy.

Don't sprinkle salt over vegetables or other foods before microwaving. The salt attracts microwave energy and can cause overcooking in spots. Instead, add salt to cooking liquid or to foods after cooking.

500 mL	broccoli florets	2 cups
500 mL	cauliflower florets	2 cups
1	small zucchini, cut in 5 mm (1/4-inch) slices	1
1	small yellow summer squash, cut in 5 mm (1/4-inch) slices	1
1	can (284 mL/10 oz) condensed chicken broth	1
6	mushrooms, halved	6
10 mL	cornstarch	2 tsp
2 mL	crushed dried basil	1/2 tsp
5 mL	white vinegar	1 tsp

Arrange broccoli in circle around rim of 30 cm (12-inch) microwaveable platter. Arrange cauliflower next to broccoli. Arrange alternate slices of zucchini and squash next to cauliflower, leaving space in centre of platter. Pour 50 mL (1/4 cup) of the broth over vegetables. Cover with vented plastic wrap; microwave at High (100% power) 5 minutes, rotating dish once.

Place mushrooms in centre of platter. Garnish with red pepper strips. Cover and microwave at High 2 minutes or until vegetables are tender-crisp. Let stand, covered, while preparing sauce.

In small microwaveable bowl, stir together remaining broth, cornstarch, basil and vinegar until smooth. Cover with vented plastic wrap; microwave at High 2 minutes or until bubbling, stirring twice during cooking. Spoon over vegetables.

Makes 6 servings.

FOOD CHOICE VALUE *per serving*

Each Serving: 1/6 of recipe

1/2 ☑ *Protein Choice*

1 ◩ *Fruits & Vegetables Choice*

8 g	Carbohydrate
5 g	Protein
1 g	Total Fat
223	kilojoules (53 Calories)

Marinated Vegetables

Here's a great way to put lots of flavor into your vegetables with very few added calories. It's great for parties, too, because everything is done in advance and the vegetables marinate until you're ready to serve them.

250 mL	*julienned carrots*	*1 cup*
250 g	*green beans, cut in 2.5 cm*	*1/2 lb*
	(1 inch) lengths; or 1 pkg (284 g/10 oz) frozen	
25 mL	*finely chopped onion*	*2 tbsp*
1	*large sweet red pepper, julienned*	*1*
1	*large zucchini, julienned*	*1*
375 mL	*vegetable or tomato juice*	*1 1/2 cups*
25 mL	*vinegar*	*2 tbsp*
15 mL	*vegetable oil*	*1 tbsp*
5 mL	*chili powder*	*1 tsp*
	Salad greens	

In 3 L (12 x 8 inch) microwaveable baking dish, combine carrots, beans and onion. Cover with vented plastic wrap; microwave at High (100% power) 4 minutes or until almost tender, stirring once.

Stir in pepper and zucchini; cover and microwave at High 4 minutes or until pepper is tender-crisp, stirring once.

In small bowl, combine vegetable juice, vinegar, oil and chili powder; pour over warm vegetables. Cover and refrigerate until chilled, at least 4 hours. Serve over salad greens.

Makes 8 servings.

Your microwave oven makes it easy to cook faster, but how can you cool foods faster? One way is to put the warm food into a bowl, then set that into a larger bowl of ice and water. If the hot food can be stirred without changing the consistency of it (such as a soup or stew), constant stirring will help cool the food even faster. Don't stir foods that might break up and become unattractive (potato salad for example).

FOOD CHOICE VALUE *per serving*

Each Serving: 1/8 of recipe

1   ◪ *Fruits & Vegetables Choice*

1/2   ◩ *Fats & Oils Choice*

8 g	*Carbohydrate*
1 g	*Protein*
2 g	*Total Fat*
202	*kilojoules (48 Calories)*

MAIN MEALS
BEEF

	Microwave	Protein	Starchy	Fruits & Vegetables	Fats & Oils	Extra	Page
Hoisin Beef Strips		3 1/2					112
Meatloaf Italiano (*Photo: p. 90*)		3		1 1/2	2		113
Hearty Maple Stew		3	1	1 1/2	1/2		114
Fajita-Style Round Steak		4		1/2			115
Szechuan-Style Beef & Broccoli Stir-Fry		4		2	1	1	116
Flank Steak with Tomato Mushroom Sauce	●	4		1	1		117
Gingered Beef		2 1/2		1/2			118
Beef Enchiladas (*Photo: p. 125*)	●	4 1/2	1	1	1		119
Greek-Style Beef Skillet (*Photo: p. 124*)		4	1 1/2				120
Mandarin Beef Stir-Fry (*Photo: p. 123*)		3		1 1/2			121
Spicy Orange Beef (*Photo: p. 123*)	●	4		1			122
Sweet & Sour Dijon-Marinated Steak	●	3 1/2		1/2			127
Sesame Strips		3					128
Beef Souvlaki		3		1/2			129
Budget Beef Rolls		3 1/2	1/2				130
Dilled Pot Roast		2					131
Meat Pie Italiano		2 1/2	1	1/2	1 1/2		132
Caribbean Kabobs		3					133

The Food Choice Values on each recipe do not include accompanying foods which are suggested in many of the recipes and shown in some of the photographs.

Hoisin Beef Strips

Although flank steak is one of the least tender cuts, it has lots of flavor and offers good value because it is boneless and has minimal fat. Cutting across the grain and marinating increases the tenderness immeasurably.

750 g	*flank or round steak*	1 1/2 lb
50 mL	*hoisin sauce*	1/4 cup
50 mL	*rice wine (sake or mirin) or dry sherry**	1/4 cup
25 mL	*soy sauce*	2 tbsp
15 mL	*sesame oil*	1 tbsp
4	*green onions, sliced*	4
5 mL	*grated gingerroot*	1 tsp

Cut flank steak across the grain into long 5 mm (1/4 inch) thick slices.

In shallow dish, combine hoisin sauce, rice wine, soy sauce, sesame oil, onions and gingerroot; add meat, stirring to coat. Cover and marinate in refrigerator 4 hours, stirring occasionally.

Thread strips lengthwise onto skewers in interlacing fashion, reserving marinade. Grill on greased grill over medium-high heat 3 to 4 minutes per side, basting with marinade.

Makes 6 servings, each 85 g/3 oz.

If using wooden skewers on the barbecue, soak skewers in water for 30 minutes before using to prevent burning.

*Ask your dietitian or doctor about the use of alcohol.

FOOD CHOICE VALUE *per serving*

Each Serving: 1/6 of recipe

3 1/2 ☑ *Protein Choices*

2 g	*Carbohydrate*
26 g	*Protein*
9 g	*Total Fat*
848	*kilojoules (202 Calories)*

Meatloaf Italiano

PHOTO ON PAGE 90.

Laced with pizza flavors, this simple skillet dish gives a new twist to old-fashioned meatloaf.

500 g	*lean ground beef*	*1 lb*
250 g	*lean ground pork*	*1/2 lb*
approx 70 g	*dry mushroom soup mix*	*1 pkg*
125 mL	*fine dry bread crumbs*	*1/2 cup*
125 mL	*finely chopped onion*	*1/2 cup*
1	*egg*	*1*
1	*can (213 mL/7.5 oz) pizza sauce*	*1*
125 g	*mozzarella, fontina or provolone cheese, sliced*	*4 oz*

Combine beef, pork, soup mix, bread crumbs, onion, egg and half of the pizza sauce; mix well. Press in 23 cm (9 inch) skillet with heat resistant handle or 23 cm (9 inch) pie plate.

Bake in 190°C (375°F) oven 40 to 45 minutes or until meat is cooked and no longer pink. Drain off fat.

Spread remaining pizza sauce over meat; arrange cheese on top. Bake 5 minutes longer. Cut into wedges to serve.

Makes 8 servings.

GOOD Source of IRON

FOOD CHOICE VALUE *per serving*

Each Serving: 1/8 of recipe

3	▢	*Protein Choices*
1 1/2	▢	*Fruits & Vegetables Choices*
2	▲	*Fats & Oils Choices*

15 g	*Carbohydrate*
21 g	*Protein*
18 g	*Total Fat*
1306	*kilojoules (311 Calories)*

Hearty Maple Stew

Flavored with maple syrup and red wine, the familiar old-fashioned stew takes on an intriguing new look. Serve with a fresh baguette of bread to complete this country kitchen favorite.

50 mL	all-purpose flour	1/4 cup
5 mL	salt	1 tsp
2 mL	ginger	1/2 tsp
1 mL	garlic powder	1/4 tsp
1 mL	pepper	1/4 tsp
1 kg	stewing beef, cut in 2.5 cm (1 inch) cubes	2 lb
50 mL	vegetable oil	3 tbsp
1	can (540 mL/19 oz) stewed tomatoes	1
2	medium onions, sliced	2
250 mL	water	1 cup
125 mL	dry red or cooking wine*	1/2 cup
50 mL	maple syrup	1/4 cup
750 mL	potato chunks	3 cups
500 mL	carrot chunks	2 cups
250 mL	sliced celery	1 cup

In bag, combine flour, salt, ginger, garlic powder and pepper; add beef and shake to coat.

In Dutch oven, brown meat in hot oil. Add tomatoes, onions, water, wine and maple syrup; bring to boil. Cover and simmer over low heat, or bake in 160°C (325°F) oven, 1-1/2 to 2 hours or until meat is tender.

Add potatoes, carrots and celery; cook 30 to 45 minutes until vegetables are tender.

Makes 8 servings, each 310 g / 11 oz.

Ask your dietitian or doctor about the use of alcohol.

FOOD CHOICE VALUE *per serving*

Each Serving: 1/8 of recipe

3	▨ *Protein Choices*
1	☐ *Starchy Choice*
1 1/2	◪ *Fruits & Vegetables Choices*
1/2	◣ *Fats & Oils Choice*
31 g	Carbohydrate
24 g	Protein
12 g	Total Fat
1394	kilojoules (332 Calories)

Fajita-Style Round Steak

Garnish with lime wedges and serve with nacho chips. Or spoon into warm flour tortillas, top with salsa and fold up to form a sandwich.

15 mL	*lime juice*	*1 tbsp*
15 mL	*chili powder*	*1 tbsp*
5 mL	*dried oregano*	*1 tsp*
2 mL	*garlic powder*	*1/2 tsp*
	Pepper	
500 g	*round steak, cut in thin strips*	*1 lb*
10 mL	*vegetable oil*	*2 tsp*
500 mL	*sliced fresh mushrooms*	*2 cups*
1	*sweet red or green pepper, cut in strips*	*1*
4	*green onions, cut in 2.5 cm (1 inch) pieces*	*4*

In shallow dish, combine lime juice, chili powder, oregano, garlic, and pepper to taste; add beef, stirring to coat. Set aside.

In nonstick skillet, heat oil over medium-high heat; sauté mushrooms and sweet pepper for 2 minutes. Remove and set aside.

Add beef to pan; cook, stirring often, until browned. Return vegetables and green onions to pan; cook, stirring constantly, until hot, about 2 minutes.

Makes 4 servings.

Chili Powder is used in many Mexican type dishes. It may also be used to spice-up stews, hamburgers, meat loaf, casseroles, etc. Use Chili Powder when you wish to dominate food flavor rather than enhance it. Use 1 to 2 tbsp for 8 cups of ground beef, noodle or rice skillet dishes.

EXCELLENT Source of **IRON**

FOOD CHOICE VALUE *per serving*

Each Serving: 1/4 of recipe

4	☑	*Protein Choices*
1/2	◨	*Fruits & Vegetables Choice*

5 g	*Carbohydrate*
28 g	*Protein*
8 g	*Total Fat*
840	*kilojoules (200 Calories)*

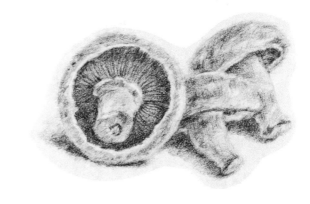

Szechuan-Style Beef and Broccoli Stir-Fry

Tender, lean steak is one of the fastest meats to cook when you're in a hurry. Serve over cooked noodles and sprinkle with peanuts for an authentic Szechuan-style meal.

20 mL	cornstarch	4 tsp
1	can (540 mL / 19 oz)* diced tomatoes	1
25 mL	soy sauce	2 tbsp
1 mL	crushed hot pepper flakes	1/4 tsp
25 mL	vegetable oil	2 tbsp
500 g	beef steak (round, sirloin, flank), cut in thin strips	1 lb
500 mL	broccoli florets	2 cups
1	can (284 mL / 10 oz) sliced water chestnuts, drained	1

Combine cornstarch, tomatoes, soy sauce and hot pepper flakes.

In large skillet, heat oil over medium-high heat. Brown beef strips on both sides, about 2 minutes.

Add tomato mixture and bring to boil; simmer, uncovered, for 5 minutes, stirring occasionally.

Stir in broccoli and water chestnuts; cook about 5 minutes longer or until broccoli is tender.

Makes 4 servings, each 365 g/13 oz.

For ease in slicing beef, place in freezer for 1 hour. Sirloin tip steak is excellent for stir-fry and more economical than sirloin steak. Slice steak across the grain for more tenderness.

*Recipe has been developed for use with 19 oz or 28 oz can sizes. Nutritional analysis based on 19 oz size only.

HIGH FIBRE

EXCELLENT Source of **IRON**

FOOD CHOICE VALUE	per serving
Each Serving : 1/4 of recipe	
4	▨ *Protein Choices*
2	▢ *Fruits & Vegetables Choices*
1	▲ *Fats & Oils Choice*
1	✛ *Extra*
24 g	*Carbohydrate*
31 g	*Protein*
16 g	*Total Fat*
1483	*kilojoules (353 Calories)*

Flank Steak with Tomato Mushroom Sauce

This simple but stylish sauce is served over a quickly grilled steak. Bake potatoes in the microwave to serve as an accompaniment.

500 g	*flank steak, scored*	*1 lb*
2 mL	*dried basil*	*1/2 tsp*
	Pepper	
25 mL	*butter or soft margarine*	*2 tbsp*
500 mL	*sliced mushrooms*	*2 cups*
1	*clove garlic, minced*	*1*
15 mL	*all-purpose flour*	*1 tbsp*
1	*can (540 mL / 19 oz)* spicy tomatoes*	*1*
1 mL	*salt*	*1/4 tsp*
25 mL	*brandy*	*2 tbsp*

Sprinkle steak with basil, and pepper to taste. Broil or grill for 15 to 18 minutes or to desired doneness.

Conventional method: Meanwhile, melt butter in saucepan over medium-high heat. Sauté mushrooms and garlic for 2 minutes or until lightly browned. Stir in flour; add tomatoes, halving with fork, and salt. Cook, stirring until mixture comes to boil; simmer 5 minutes, stirring occasionally. Stir in brandy.

Microwave method: Place butter, mushrooms and garlic in 2 L (8-cup) microwaveable bowl. Cover with waxed paper. Microwave at High (100% power) 3 minutes, stirring once. Add flour, then tomatoes and salt. Cover and microwave at High 6 to 7 minutes until bubbly and thickened, stirring every 2 minutes. Stir in brandy.

Both methods: Slice steak, diagonally across the grain into thin strips. Spoon sauce over steak.

Makes 4 servings, each 365 g/13 oz.

MICROWAVEABLE

This sauce could be prepared in the microwave while the steak cooks.

*Recipe has been developed for use with 19 oz or 28 oz can sizes. Nutritional analysis based on 19 oz size only.

FOOD CHOICE VALUE *per serving*

Each Serving: 1/4 of recipe

4	▨	*Protein Choices*
1	▧	*Fruits & Vegetables Choice*
1	▲	*Fats & Oils Choice*

12 g	*Carbohydrate*
31 g	*Protein*
16 g	*Total Fat*
1382	*kilojoules (329 Calories)*

Gingered Beef

Be sure to have all the ingredients prepared before you start cooking. Serve with hot cooked pasta or rice tossed with a few drops of hot pepper sauce

15 mL	*vegetable oil*	*1 tbsp*
1	*medium sweet green pepper, thinly sliced*	*1*
50 mL	*chopped onion*	*1/4 cup*
250 mL	*sliced mushrooms*	*1 cup*
500 g	*flank or round steak, thinly sliced*	*1 lb*
15 mL	*water*	*1 tbsp*
15 mL	*soy sauce*	*1 tbsp*
1 mL	*ground ginger*	*1/4 tsp*
0.5 mL	*garlic powder*	*1/8 tsp*
15 mL	*cornstarch*	*1 tbsp*

In skillet, heat oil over medium-high heat; sauté green pepper, onion and mushrooms until tender-crisp. Remove vegetables from pan and set aside.

Add steak and cook, stirring, until browned. Add water, soy sauce, ginger and garlic powder; cover and simmer for 5 minutes or until meat is tender. Stir in vegetables.

Combine cornstarch with 15 mL (1 tbsp) water; add to meat mixture and cook, stirring, until thickened.

Makes 6 servings, each 115 g/4 oz.

Ground Ginger is very versatile and excellent in combination with other spices. Use in sauces, soups, oriental dishes, all red meats, most vegetables. Ground Ginger may be substituted for Whole Ginger in most recipes:1 tsp Ground Ginger is about the same as 10 pieces whole ginger(the size of shelled peanuts).

FOOD CHOICE VALUE *per serving*

Each Serving: 1/6 of recipe

2 1/2 ☑ *Protein Choices*

1/2 ◻ *Fruits & Vegetables Choice*

3 g	*Carbohydrate*
17 g	*Protein*
8 g	*Total Fat*
651	*kilojoules (155 Calories)*

Beef Enchiladas

Say "Si" to the wonderful tastes of Mexico with these delightful and nutritious enchiladas that are perfectly at home as appetizers or as a main course. An excellent source of both Calcium and Iron.

PHOTO ON PAGE 125.

500 mL	*chopped cooked roast beef (preferably rare or medium-rare)*	2 cups
2 mL	*salt*	1/2 tsp
2 mL	*ground cumin*	1/2 tsp
250 mL	*taco sauce*	1 cup
1	*can (113 mL/4 oz) green chilies, drained and chopped*	1
1	*pkg (213 g/17.5 oz) frozen crisp corn tortillas, thawed*	1
250 mL	*shredded sharp Cheddar cheese*	1 cup

Season beef with salt and cumin.

In 500 mL (2 cup) glass measure, combine taco sauce and chilies; cover and microwave at High (100% power) 2 to 3 minutes or until hot.

Cover each tortilla with 25 mL (2 tbsp) sauce. Top each with 50 mL (1/4 cup) beef and 15 mL (1 tbsp) cheese. Fold shells around filling; arrange, seam side up, in 30 x 20 cm (12- x 8-inch) microwaveable dish. Press top edges together.

Pour remaining sauce over top. Cover with waxed paper. Microwave at High 4 to 6 minutes or until heated through. Sprinkle with remaining cheese. Let stand 2 minutes before serving.

Makes 4 servings, each 225 g/8 oz.

FOOD CHOICE VALUE *per serving*

Each Serving: 1/4 of recipe

4 1/2	☑	*Protein Choices*
1	☐	*Starchy Choice*
1	◨	*Fruits & Vegetables Choice*
1	▲	*Fats & Oils Choice*

28 g	*Carbohydrate*
33 g	*Protein*
18 g	*Total Fat*
1697	*kilojoules (404 Calories)*

Greek-Style Beef Skillet

Tender pieces of beef combine with the tempting flavors of the Mediterranean for a quick-to-fix meal. Serve over cooked rice.

PHOTO ON PAGE 124.

500 g	flank or sirloin steak	1 lb
25 mL	vegetable oil	2 tbsp
1	medium onion, sliced	1
1	clove garlic, minced	1
1	can (540 mL / 19 oz)* stewed tomatoes	1
25 mL	lemon juice	2 tbsp
1 mL	ground cumin	1/4 tsp
0.5 mL	cinnamon	1/8 tsp
15 mL	cornstarch	1 tbsp
125 mL	crumbled feta cheese† (optional)	1/2 cup

Flank steak is very tender when cooked this way. Olives would be an interesting addition to enhance the theme.

*Recipe has been developed for use with 19 oz or 28 oz can sizes. Nutritional analysis based on 19 oz size only.

†Not included in Food Choice Value.

Slice steak thinly across the grain. In large skillet, heat oil over medium-high heat; brown beef on both sides and remove from pan.

Sauté onion and garlic in pan drippings 2 minutes; drain off fat. Stir in tomatoes, lemon juice, cumin and cinnamon; bring to boil.

Simmer, uncovered, 10 minutes.

Dissolve cornstarch in 15 mL (1 tbsp) water; stir into pan and cook until thickened. Stir in beef and heat through. Sprinkle with feta cheese (if using).

Makes 4 servings, each 250 g/9 oz.

FOOD CHOICE VALUE *per serving*

Each Serving: 1/4 of recipe

4 ☑ *Protein Choices*
1 1/2 ☐ *Starchy Choices*

14 g	Carbohydrate
27 g	Protein
13 g	Total Fat
1180	kilojoules (281 Calories)

Mandarin Beef Stir-Fry

PHOTO ON PAGE 123.

Mandarin oranges and orange juice perk up this Oriental stir-fry. Keep a bottle of hoisin sauce in the refrigerator and add a splash to any stir-frys for extra flavour. Serve over hot fluffy rice.

500 g	*round or sirloin tip steak,*	*1 lb*
	cut in 1 x 5 cm (1/4 x 2 inch) strips	
15 mL	*Worcestershire sauce*	*1 tbsp*
50 mL	*soy sauce*	*1/4 cup*
125 mL	*orange juice*	*1/2 cup*
1 mL	*ground ginger*	*1/4 tsp*
1 mL	*garlic powder*	*1/4 tsp*
25 mL	*vegetable oil*	*2 tbsp*
1	*medium red onion, sliced*	*1*
500 mL	*snow peas*	*2 cups*
250 mL	*fresh mushrooms, sliced*	*1 cup*
1	*sweet green pepper, sliced*	*1*
1	*can (284 mI /10 oz) mandarin oranges, drained*	*1*
25 mL	*cornstarch*	*2 tbsp*

Place beef in large shallow dish. Combine Worcestershire sauce, soy sauce, orange juice, ginger and garlic powder; pour over beef and stir. Set aside.

In wok or skillet, heat oil over medium-high heat; stir-fry onion, snow peas, mushrooms and green pepper for 2 minutes. Move vegetables to side of wok.

Drain beef, reserving marinade. Stir-fry beef until no longer pink; mix with vegetables. Add orange segments.

Combine reserved marinade with cornstarch; add to wok and cook just until thickened.

Makes 5 servings, each 250 g/9 oz.

HIGH FIBRE

EXCELLENT Source of **IRON**

FOOD CHOICE VALUE *per serving*

Each Serving: 1/5 of recipe

3	☑ *Protein Choices*
1 1/2	◨ *Fruits & Vegetables Choices*

18 g	*Carbohydrate*
24 g	*Protein*
10 g	*Total Fat*
1063	*kilojoules (253 Calories)*

Spicy Orange Beef

This is a quick stir-fry with the refreshing zest of orange and the spice of hot pepper. Serve over hot fluffy rice or egg noodles. Don't forget the chop sticks!

PHOTO ON PAGE 123.

500 g	*lean round or sirloin tip steak*	*1 lb*
4	*green onions, sliced diagonally in 1 cm (1/2-inch) pieces*	*4*
25 mL	*rice wine (sake or mirin) or dry sherry*	*2 tbsp*
25 mL	*soy sauce*	*2 tbsp*
5 mL	*grated gingerroot*	*1 tsp*
1	*clove garlic, minced*	*1*
2 mL	*hot pepper flakes*	*1/2 tsp*
125 mL	*orange juice*	*1/2 cup*
15 mL	*cornstarch*	*1 tbsp*
	Grated rind of 2 oranges	
15 mL	*sesame oil*	*1 tbsp*

Slice beef across the grain into 5 cm x 5mm (2- x 1/4-inch) strips. In bowl just large enough to hold beef, combine onions, rice wine, soy sauce, ginger, garlic and hot pepper flakes. Add beef and toss to coat; marinate 30 minutes.

When slicing the beef into thin strips, it's much easier if the meat is only partially thawed.

In 250 mL (1 cup) glass measure, combine orange juice, cornstarch and orange rind; microwave at High (100% power) for 1 to 1-1/2 minutes, stirring partway through, or until boiling and thickened. Set aside.

In 2 L (8-cup) microwaveable casserole, heat sesame oil at High for 1 minute. Stir in beef mixture; cover and microwave at Medium (50% power) for 4 minutes, stirring halfway through.

Stir in orange mixture; cover and microwave at Medium for 4 to 6 minutes, stirring partway through, or until beef is no longer pink.

Makes 4 servings, each 170 g/6 oz.

FOOD CHOICE VALUE *per serving*

Each Serving: 1/4 of recipe

4	☑	*Protein Choices*
1	◩	*Fruits & Vegetables Choice*

11 g	*Carbohydrate*
27 g	*Protein*
8 g	*Total Fat*
979	*kilojoules (233 Calories)*

Mandarin Beef Stir-Fry (p.121)

Spicy Orange Beef (p.122)

Greek-Style Beef Skillet (p.120)

Beef Enchiladas (p.119)

Chili Con Carne (p.138)

Pork Medallions with Dill (p.136)

Quick Cacciatore Stew (p.135)

Orange Pork Piccata (p.137)

Sweet & Sour Dijon-Marinated Steak

This tangy sweet and sour marinade imparts a taste of the French countryside, while turning medium or less tender cuts of steak into melt-in your-mouth morsels.

500 g	*flank or round steak*	*1 lb*
50 mL	*red wine vinegar*	*1/4 cup*
25 mL	*vegetable oil*	*2 tbsp*
25 mL	*liquid honey*	*2 tbsp*
15 mL	*Dijon mustard*	*1 tbsp*
2	*cloves garlic, minced*	*2*
	Grated rind and juice of 1 orange or lemon	

Score flank steak across the grain on both sides. If using round steak, pierce all over with fork. Place in shallow dish.

In small saucepan, combine vinegar, oil, honey, mustard, garlic, orange rind and juice; cook over medium heat until just heated through and blended. (Alternately, microwave in 500 mL/2-cup glass measure at High/100% power/1 to 1-1/2 minutes, stirring partway through.) Let cool slightly; pour over meat, turning to coat both sides. Marinate in refrigerator 4 hours, turning several times.

Grill steak on greased grill over medium-high heat 6 to 8 minutes per side or until desired doneness. To serve, carve on diagonal across the grain into thin slices.

Makes 4 servings, each 85 g/3 oz.

FOOD CHOICE VALUE *per serving*

Each Serving: 1/4 of recipe

3 1/2 ☑ *Protein Choices*

1/2 ◼ *Fruits & Vegetables Choice*

---

4 g	*Carbohydrate*
26 g	*Protein*
10 g	*Total Fat*
890	*kilojoules (212 Calories)*

Sesame Strips

Sesame oil adds an Oriental flavor to this delectable meat.
Serve with rice and grilled vegetables. Add sesame seeds if desired.

500 g	*inside or outside round,*	*1 lb*
	sirloin tip, blade or flank steak	
50 mL	*soy sauce*	*1/4 cup*
25 mL	*rice wine (sake or mirin) or dry sherry*	*2 tbsp*
5 mL	*sesame oil*	*1 tsp*
2	*green onions, finely chopped*	*2*
15 mL	*chopped gingerroot*	*1 tbsp*
2	*cloves garlic, minced*	*2*

Cut steak across the grain into long slices, 5 mm (1/4 inch) thick.

In shallow dish, combine soy sauce, rice wine, sesame oil, onions, gingerroot and garlic; add beef, stirring to coat. Cover and marinate in refrigerator 4 hours, stirring occasionally.

Thread strips lengthwise onto skewers in interlacing fashion. Lightly grease grill. Grill over medium heat (turning often), for 8 to 12 minutes, or until desired doneness.

Makes 4 servings.

Slicing less tender cuts of beef thinly across the grain and marinating it maximizes tenderness and flavor.

GOOD Source of IRON

FOOD CHOICE VALUE	*per serving*
Each Serving: 1/4 of recipe	
3	☑ *Protein Choices*

2 g	*Carbohydrate*
22 g	*Protein*
5 g	*Total Fat*
643	*kilojoules (153 Calories)*

Beef Souvlaki

Serve this traditional Greek favorite on a bed of rice with any Greek salad combination of tomato, green pepper, cucumber, black olives and feta cheese.

Rosemary is a sweet, fragrant herb that resembles the look and scent of pine needles, is excellent in lamb dishes, soups, stews, marinades, poached and broiled fish or sea food. Use in preparing a variety of meats. Sprinkle over coals when barbecuing meats.

500 g	*inside or outside round, sirloin tip, or blade steak*	*1 lb*
50 mL	*lemon juice*	*1/4 cup*
25 mL	*olive or vegetable oil*	*2 tbsp*
2	*cloves garlic, minced*	*2*
5 mL	*crushed dried rosemary*	*1 tsp*
5 mL	*dried oregano*	*1 tsp*
1 mL	*pepper*	*1/4 tsp*

YOGURT SAUCE

125 mL	*grated peeled cucumber*	*1/2 cup*
125 mL	*plain low-fat yogurt*	*1/2 cup*
25 mL	*chopped fresh parsley*	*2 tbsp*
1	*clove garlic, minced*	*1*

Cut meat into 2.5 cm (1-inch) cubes. In bowl just large enough to hold meat, combine lemon juice, oil, garlic, rosemary, oregano and pepper. Add meat, stirring to coat. Cover and marinate in refrigerator 4 hours, stirring occasionally.

Thread meat loosely onto skewers. Grill on greased grill over medium heat for 10 to 15 minutes or until desired doneness, turning often.

Yogurt Sauce: Meanwhile, in small bowl, combine cucumber, yogurt, parsley and garlic; serve with meat.

Makes 4 servings, each 112 g/4 oz.

FOOD CHOICE VALUE *per serving*

Each Serving : 1/4 of recipe

3   ☑ *Protein Choices*

1/2   ◻ *Fruits & Vegetables Choice*

---

4 g   Carbohydrate

23 g   Protein

9 g   Total Fat

798   kilojoules *(190 Calories)*

Budget Beef Rolls

Fresh garden herbs, mushrooms and bread crumbs make a tasty, budget-stretching filling for grilled beef rolls. The rolls can be prepared ahead and refrigerated, ready for last-minute grilling. Serve with grilled vegetables, fresh corn or salad.

4	*thin round sirloin tip or blade steaks (each 125 g/1/4 lb)*	*4*
25 mL	*olive or vegetable oil*	*2 tbsp*
1	*small onion, chopped*	*1*
125 mL	*chopped mushrooms*	*1/2 cup*
250 mL	*soft fresh bread crumbs*	*1 cup*
50 mL	*chopped fresh parsley*	*1/4 cup*
5 mL	*chopped fresh thyme (or 2 mL/1/2 tsp dried)*	*1 tsp*
Pinch	*crumbled dried rosemary*	*Pinch*
	Salt and pepper	
15 mL	*lemon juice*	*1 tbsp*
1	*clove garlic, crushed*	*1*

Pound steaks to even 5 mm (1/4-inch) thickness.

In small skillet, heat 15 mL (1 tbsp) of the oil; cook onion until softened. Add mushrooms and sauté briefly. Stir in bread crumbs, parsley, thyme, rosemary, and salt and pepper to taste. Divide mixture among steaks, leaving 1 cm (1/2-inch) border and pressing mixture into steaks. Starting with narrow edge, roll up and tie with string.

Combine remaining oil, lemon juice and garlic; brush all over rolls. Let stand for 15 minutes.

Grill on greased grill over medium heat for 10 to 15 minutes or until browned to desired doneness. To serve, remove string and cut into slices.

Makes 4 servings, each 112 g/4 oz.

For easy preparation, ask the butcher to slice steaks thinly or use fast-fry steaks.

EXCELLENT Source of IRON

FOOD CHOICE VALUE *per serving*

Each Serving: 1/4 of recipe

3 1/2 ☑ *Protein Choices*

1/2 ☐ *Starchy Choice*

10 g	*Carbohydrate*
27 g	*Protein*
11 g	*Total Fat*
1033	*kilojoules (246 Calories)*

Dilled Pot Roast

Here's a great staple recipe that enhances any cut of roast.
The dillweed, mustard and wine creates a flavorful mixture that
will simmer the meat to perfection, while you prepare fluffy mashed
potatoes and tender-crisp green beans.

To make a pot roast as lean as possible, trim off all visible fat. Use a heavy saucepan or Dutch oven for the long, slow simmering.

Dill is available as Seed and Weed (leaves). Dill Weed is bright green with a more delicate flavor than Dill Seed, which has a pungent aromatic flavor. Dill Seed is used mainly in pickles, but may be used in Egg and Cheese dishes, soups, stews, etc. Cumin Seed is often used interchangeably.

*Ask your dietitian or doctor about the use of alcohol.

5 mL	vegetable oil	1 tsp
1.5 kg	boneless cross-rib, blade or shoulder roast	3 lb
15 mL	prepared mustard	1 tbsp
10 mL	dried dillweed	2 tsp
1	bay leaf	1
12	black peppercorns	12
12	whole allspice	12
	Juice and rind of half a lemon	
250 mL	dry red wine*	1 cup
1	onion, sliced	1

In heavy saucepan, heat oil; brown roast on all sides. Spread mustard over roast.

Combine dillweed, bay leaf, peppercorns, allspice, lemon juice and rind and wine; pour over roast. Add onion. Cover and simmer over low heat for 2 hours or until, tender.

Makes 10 servings, each 70 g / 2 1/2 oz.

FOOD CHOICE VALUE *per serving*

Each Serving: 1/10 of recipe

2   ☑ *Protein Choices*

0 g	Carbohydrate
16 g	Protein
3 g	Total Fat
395	kilojoules (94 Calories)

Meat Pie Italiano

Your kids will never want just plain pizza again after they've had
a taste of this tantalizing treat. Makes a complete meal when served
with a salad and crusty rolls.

375 g	*lean ground beef*	*3/4 lb*
1	*can (213 mL/7-1/2 oz) pizza sauce*	*1*
50 mL	*chopped onion*	*1/4 cup*
50 mL	*fine dry bread crumbs*	*1/4 cup*
4 mL	*salt*	*3/4 tsp*
375 mL	*cooked rice*	*1 1/2 cups*
250 mL	*shredded mozzarella cheese*	*1 cup*
25 mL	*grated Parmesan cheese*	*2 tbsp*
2	*eggs, beaten*	*2*

Combine beef, 75 mL (1/3 cup) of the pizza sauce, onion, bread
crumbs and salt; press onto sides and bottom of 23 cm (9-inch) pie
plate to form shell. Bake in 180°C (350°F) oven 15 minutes. Drain.

Combine rice, mozzarella cheese, Parmesan cheese and eggs; fill
meat shell. Spread remaining pizza sauce on top. Bake 30 to 35
minutes longer or until set. Let stand 5 minutes before cutting.

Makes 6 servings, each 168 g/6 oz.

FOOD CHOICE VALUE	*per serving*
Each Serving: 1/6 of recipe	
2 1/2 ☑ *Protein Choices*	
1 ☐ *Starchy Choice*	
1/2 ◪ *Fruits & Vegetables Choice*	
1 1/2 ▲ *Fats & Oils Choices*	
21 g	*Carbohydrate*
20 g	*Protein*
15 g	*Total Fat*
1252	*kilojoules (298 Calories)*

Caribbean Kabobs

Pineapple and lime provide a flavor of the tropics. Serve with rice, grilled zucchini, and sliced mango or papaya for dessert.

When barbecuing, cooking times can vary because of the temperature of the grill, weather and wind conditions.

750 g	inside or outside round, sirloin tip or blade steak	1 1/2 lb
250 mL	pineapple juice	1 cup
	Juice and rind of 1 lime	
1	small onion, finely chopped	1
2	cloves garlic, minced	2
5 mL	chopped gingerroot	1 tsp
1 mL	hot pepper sauce or hot pepper flakes	1/4 tsp

Cut beef into 2.5 cm (1-inch) cubes. In bowl just large enough to hold meat, combine pineapple juice, lime juice and rind, onion, garlic, gingerroot and hot pepper sauce; add beef, stirring to coat. Cover and marinate in refrigerator 4 hours, stirring occasionally.

Thread beef loosely onto skewers. Grill on greased grill over medium heat for 10 to 15 minutes or until desired doneness, turning often.

Makes 6 servings, each 168 g/6 oz.

FOOD CHOICE VALUE *per serving*

Each Serving: 1/6 of recipe

3   ☑ *Protein Choices*

2 g	*Carbohydrate*
22 g	*Protein*
5 g	*Total Fat*
596	*kilojoules (142 Calories)*

MAIN MEALS
PORK

	Microwave	Protein	Starchy	Fruits & Vegetables	Fats & Oils	Extra	Page
Quick Cacciatore Stew *(Photo: p. 126)*		3		1 1/2			135
Pork Medallion with Dijon Dill *(Photo: p. 125)*	•	4		1/2			136
Orange Pork Piccata *(Photo: p. 126)*		1 1/2	1/2		2		137
Chili Con Carne *(Photo: p. 125)*	•	2 1/2	1		1		138
Cajun Pork Chops and Rice *(Photo: p. 87)*		1 1/2	2	1 1/2	1/2		139
Pork Chops with Tomato Salsa		3 1/2		1	1/2		140
Home-Style Pork Roast		3 1/2					141
Hungarian Goulash	•	3 1/2		1/2	1		142
Orange Pork Loin Chops		3 1/2		1/2	1		143
Pork Schnitzel with Vegetables		4		1 1/2			144
Marinated Pork Steak		3 1/2					145
Pork Tenderloin with Apricot Sauce		2		1	1/2		146
Roast Pork Stuffed with Vegetables		3 1/2				1	147
Mediterranean Pork Kabobs		3 1/2		1	1 1/2		148
Pork Pepper Steak	•	3			1		149
Cajun Breaded Pork		2	1		1		150
Fried Rice with Pork & Veggies *(Photo: p. 159)*		2	1 1/2		1		151

The Food Choice Values on each recipe do not include accompanying foods which are suggested in many of the recipes and shown in some of the photographs.

Quick Cacciatore Stew

This pork stew with an Italian flair is simple to prepare.
Serve with fluffy mashed potatoes, noodles or crusty Italian bread.

15 mL	*vegetable oil*	*1 tbsp*
1	*medium onion, coarsely chopped*	*1*
2	*cloves garlic, minced*	*2*
1	*stalk celery, coarsely chopped*	*1*
2	*carrots, thinly sliced*	*2*
10	*mushrooms, sliced*	*10*
1	*can (540 mL/19 oz) tomatoes, crushed*	*1*
5 mL	*Italian seasoning*	*1 tsp*
500 g	*boneless pork shoulder, trimmed and cut in bite-size pieces*	*1 lb*
	Salt and pepper	

In medium pot, heat oil over medium heat. Add pork and brown
on all sides, stirring occasionally. Remove pork and set aside.

Reduce heat to medium-low; cook onion, garlic, celery and
carrots, stirring occasionally, until onions are soft, about 5 minutes.

Stir in mushrooms, tomatoes, Italian seasoning and pork; cover
and simmer for 30 minutes, stirring occasionally. Season with salt
and pepper to taste.

Makes 4 servings.

PHOTO ON PAGE 126.

*Italian seasoning may be
bought pre-mixed, or can be
any combination of oregano,
rosemary, thyme and basil.*

GOOD Source of IRON

FOOD CHOICE VALUE *per serving*

Each Serving: 1/4 of recipe

3	☑	*Protein Choices*
1 1/2	◼	*Fruits & Vegetables Choices*

---

15 g	*Carbohydrate*
26 g	*Protein*
9 g	*Total Fat*
932	*kilojoules (222 Calories)*

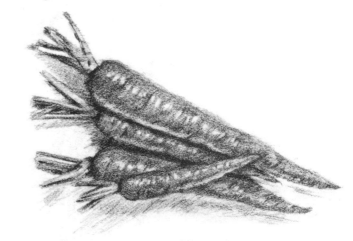

Pork Medallions with Dijon Dill

If you prefer to serve the sauce warm, place it in a heatproof measure and warm it in hot (not boiling) water for 2 to 3 minutes, being careful that it doesn't cook or curdle.

PHOTO ON PAGE 125.

1	*large pork tenderloin, sliced crosswise*	*1*
15 mL	*vegetable oil*	*1 tbsp*
2 mL	*garlic salt*	*1/2 tsp*
1 mL	*pepper*	*1/4 tsp*
125 mL	*plain low fat yogurt*	*1/2 cup*
15 mL	*dijon mustard*	*1 tbsp*
2 mL	*dried dillweed*	*1/2 tsp*
2 mL	*granulated sugar*	*1/2 tsp*

To make medallions, place each piece of pork, cut side down, on flat surface; cover with waxed paper and flatten with bottom of saucepan, mallet or cleaver to 5 mm (1/4 inch) thickness. Heat oil in skillet over medium-high heat; brown pork for 3 to 4 minutes per side. Remove to warm platter; season both sides with garlic salt and pepper.

Meanwhile, combine yogurt, mustard, dillweed and sugar; mix well. Serve sauce with pork medallions.

Microwave method: Prepare pork medallions as in recipe. Omit oil. Microwave pork and 15 mL (1 tbsp) white wine, in shallow microwaveable dish, covered, at Medium (50% power) for 5 to 7 minutes, turning pork over halfway through cooking time. Season as in recipe.

Prepare sauce as in recipe; microwave at Medium (50% power) for 1 to 2 minutes.

Makes 2 servings.

FOOD CHOICE VALUE *per serving*

Each Serving: 1/2 of recipe

4 ☑ *Protein Choices*

1/2 ◨ *Fruits & Vegetables Choice*

4 g	*Carbohydrate*
28 g	*Protein*
9 g	*Total Fat*
895	*kilojoules (213 Calories)*

Orange Pork Piccata

PHOTO ON PAGE 126.

This dish is so quick and easy that you'll have plenty of time left to sit back and enjoy it.

50 mL	all-purpose flour	1/4 cup
Pinch	each, salt and pepper	Pinch
45 mL	butter or soft margarine	3 tbsp
5 mL	vegetable oil	1 tsp
250 g	thinly sliced pork (leg or loin), or fast-fry boneless chops 3 to 5 mm (1/8 to 1/4 inch) thick (about 8 loins)	1/2 lb
125 mL	strained fresh orange juice	1/2 cup
Pinch	crumbled dried sage	Pinch
5 mL	all-purpose flour	1 tsp
5 mL	cold water	1 tsp
25 mL	minced fresh parsley	2 tbsp

Season flour with salt and pepper. Melt 25 mL (2 tbsp) of the butter with oil in heavy skillet over high heat. Dredge pork in flour and shake off excess; cook for 1 1/2 minutes on each side. Remove from pan; keep warm.

Pour off pan drippings and discard. Add 50 mL (1/4 cup) of the orange juice to skillet; boil for 1 minute, scraping up browned bits. Add remaining orange juice and sage; season with salt and pepper. Mix 5 mL (1 tsp) flour with water; stir into skillet and cook until thickened, about 1 minute. Remove from heat; swirl in remaining butter. Pour in any juices from meat. Drizzle sauce over meat; sprinkle with parsley.

Makes 4 servings.

FOOD CHOICE VALUE *per serving*

Each Serving: 1/4 of recipe

1 1/2 ☑ *Protein Choices*
1/2 ☐ *Starchy Choice*
2 ◣ *Fats & Oils Choices*

9 g Carbohydrate
13 g Protein
13 g Total Fat
865 kilojoules (206 Calories)

Chili Con Carne

Top each serving with 15 mL (1 tbsp) yogurt and some shredded Cheddar cheese. Serve with tortilla chips, fresh rolls or buttered toast.

PHOTO ON PAGE 125.

500 g	ground pork	1 lb
1	*large onion, chopped*	*1*
1	*sweet green pepper, diced (optional)*	*1*
2 to 5 mL	*hot pepper flakes(optional)*	*1/2 to 1 tsp*
1	*can (540 mL/19 oz) tomatoes (undrained), chopped*	*1*
1	*can (398 mL/14 oz) tomato sauce*	*1*
5 to 10 mL	*chili powder*	*2 to 3 tsp*
15 mL	*Worcestershire sauce*	*1 tbsp*
1 mL	*cumin*	*1/4 tsp*
1	*can (398 mL/14 oz) kidney beans*	*1*

In large deep skillet or Dutch oven, cook pork, onion and green pepper (if using) over medium heat 5 to 10 minutes, until onions are soft and meat is browned.

Add hot pepper flakes (if using), tomatoes, tomato sauce, chili powder, Worcestershire sauce and cumin; simmer for 20 minutes. Add kidney beans, simmer 10 more minutes.

Microwave method: In large microwaveable bowl, microwave pork, onion and green pepper, covered, at High (100% power) for 5 to 7 minutes or until no longer pink, stirring once. Drain. Add remaining ingredients; cover and microwave at High for 5 to 6 minutes, then at Medium-Low (30% power) for 10 to 15 minutes, stirring twice during cooking time.

Makes 6 to 8 servings.

FOOD CHOICE VALUE *per serving*

Each Serving: 1/8 of recipe

2 1/2	☑	*Protein Choices*
1	☐	*Starchy Choice*
1	▲	*Fats & Oils Choice*

24 g	*Carbohydrate*
20 g	*Protein*
11 g	*Total Fat*
1117	*kilojoules (266 Calories)*

Cajun Pork Chops and Rice

The sweet and savory flavors of this Louisiana one-pot meal are bound to please hearty appetites. Just add a salad.

4	pork loin chops	4
1	can (540 mL/19 oz)* cajun spice stewed tomatoes plus 75 mL/1/3 cup water	1
50 mL	dry white wine† or water	1/4 cup
5 mL	dried marjoram	1 tsp
2 mL	dried thyme	1/2 tsp
1 mL	salt	1/4 tsp
1 mL	pepper	1/4 tsp
175 mL	long-grain white rice	3/4 cup
50 mL	raisins	1/4 cup

Trim fat from pork chops; use trimmings to grease large skillet over medium-heat, then discard. Brown pork chops on both sides.

Add tomatoes, water, wine, marjoram, thyme, salt and pepper; bring to boil. Stir in rice and raisins. Cover and simmer over low heat 25 to 30 minutes or until pork is no longer pink inside and rice is tender.

Makes 4 servings.

PHOTO ON PAGE 87.

Spicy

Recipe has been developed for use with 19 oz or 28 oz can sizes. Nutritional analysis based on 19 oz size only.

If using 28 oz. can size, do not add 75 mL/1/3 cup water.

†Ask your dietitian or doctor about the use of alcohol.

FOOD CHOICE VALUE *per serving*

Each Serving: 1/4 of recipe

1 1/2 ☑ *Protein Choices*

2 ☐ *Starchy Choices*

1 1/2 ◧ *Fruits & Vegetables Choices*

1/2 ▲ *Fats & Oils Choice*

45 g   *Carbohydrate*

17 g   *Protein*

7 g   *Total Fat*

1319   *kilojoules (314 Calories)*

Pork Chops with Tomato Salsa

For this dish, the tomato salsa may be prepared ahead, to allow
flavors to develop. Serve with "Two step Tomato Salsa" (page 40)
and tortilla chips as an appetizer.

1	can (540 mL /19 oz)* mexican spice stewed tomatoes	1
2	green onions, sliced	2
1	clove garlic, minced	1
15 mL	red wine vinegar	1 tbsp
1 mL	crushed hot pepper flakes (optional)	1/4 tsp
1 mL	salt	1/4 tsp
15 mL	vegetable oil	1 tbsp
500 g	boneless thin pork chops	1 lb
25 mL	all-purpose flour	2 tbsp

In non-metallic bowl, combine tomatoes, green onions, garlic,
vinegar, hot pepper flakes and salt.

Heat oil in large skillet over medium-high heat. Brown pork chops
on both sides.

Stir flour into pan juices; add tomato mixture, stirring well. Simmer,
uncovered, over low heat about 15 minutes or until pork is tender
and no longer pink inside, stirring occasionally.

Makes 4 servings, each 225 g/8 oz.

*If milder flavor is preferred, adjust
quantity of crushed red pepper or
omit entirely.*

**Recipe has been developed for use
with 19 oz or 28 oz can sizes.
Nutritional analysis based on 19 oz
size only.*

FOOD CHOICE VALUE	*per serving*
Each Serving : 1/4 of recipe	
3 1/2 ☑ *Protein Choices*	
1 ◀ *Fruits & Vegetables Choice*	
1/2 ▲ *Fats & Oils Choice*	
13 g	*Carbohydrate*
26 g	*Protein*
14 g	*Total Fat*
1160	*kilojoules (276 Calories)*

Home-Style Pork Roast

This pork roast is so easy to prepare, and the seasonings will fill your kitchen with a wonderful aroma.

1	*boneless pork double loin or shoulder roast*	*1*
	(1 to 1 1/2 kg/2 1/2 to 3 lb)	
2	*cloves garlic*	*2*
2	*bay leaves*	*2*
250 mL	*apple juice*	*1 cup*
2 mL	*each onion powder, celery salt*	*1/2 tsp*
	and crushed dried rosemary	

Place roast in small ovenproof dish. Cut garlic cloves in half; rub cut surface over roast. Cut four 5 mm (1/4 inch) pockets into top of roast and insert garlic halves. Place bay leaves beside roast. Pour in apple juice. Sprinkle meat with onion powder, celery salt and rosemary.

Cover dish loosely with foil; roast in 160°C (325°F) oven for 40 minutes. Uncover and roast for 35 minutes longer or until meat thermometer registers 70°C (160°F). Do not overcook.

Remove from oven and let stand, covered with foil, about 10 minutes before carving. Spoon pan juices over slices when serving.

Makes 4 servings, each 90 g/3 oz.

Another popular way to cook pork roast is to sprinkle it with a package of onion soup mix, then cook it in foil.

Bay Leaves have a strong distinct flavor that is almost bitter. Use in soups, chowders, pickling, steaming or poaching fish and shellfish. Strength of flavor increases with amount used and cooking time. Remove from food when cooking time has elapsed.

FOOD CHOICE VALUE *per serving*

Each Serving: 1/4 of recipe

3 1/2 ☑ *Protein Choices*

0 g	*Carbohydrate*
24 g	*Protein*
10 g	*Total Fat*
815	*kilojoules (194 Calories)*

ROAST TYPE	COOKING MIN. per pound (500 g)		SERVINGS per pound (500 g)	
	Bone-in	Boneless	Bone-in	Boneless
Loin	30-35	30-35	2-3	3-4
Shoulder Butt		40-45	2-3	3-4
Picnic Shoulder	30-35	35-40	2-3	3-4

Hungarian Goulash

Now here's a meal that is perfect on a cold winter day after the family has been skating or cross country skiing. An old-world favorite that sticks to your ribs and warms you up with a comforting goodness. Serve with dumplings or over egg noodles.

15 mL	*butter or soft margarine*	*1 tbsp*
125 mL	*chopped onion*	*1/2 cup*
6	*large mushrooms, quartered*	*6*
750 g	*cubed trimmed pork shoulder or leg, (1 – 1.25 kg/2 – 2 1/2 lb untrimmed)*	*1 1/2 lb*
15 mL	*paprika*	*1 tbsp*
1	*clove garlic, minced*	*1*
125 mL	*beef bouillon*	*1/2 cup*
25 mL	*red wine vinegar*	*2 tbsp*
25 mL	*tomato paste*	*2 tbsp*
10 mL	*caraway seeds*	*2 tsp*
25 mL	*all-purpose flour*	*2 tbsp*
125 mL	*sour cream or yogurt*	*1/2 cup*

In a 2 L (8 cup) casserole dish, combine butter, onion and mushrooms. Cover and microwave at High (100% power) for 3 minutes, stirring halfway through cooking time.

Add pork, paprika, garlic, bouillon, vinegar, tomato paste and caroway seeds; cover and microwave at Medium-Low (30% power) for 15 minutes. Mix well and microwave another 15 minutes.

Remove 125 mL (1/2 cup) hot liquid and stir in flour. Stir flour mixture into goulash and microwave 15 minutes. Stir in sour cream or yogurt.

Makes 6 servings.

When microwaving do not salt meat before cooking. Salt added directly to meat tends to dry it out. Season after cooking or add salt to cooking liquid.

FOOD CHOICE VALUE	*per serving*

Each Serving: 1/6 of recipe

3 1/2 ☑ *Protein Choices*

1/2 ◪ *Fruits & Vegetables Choice*

1 ▲ *Fats & Oils Choice*

7 g	*Carbohydrate*
25 g	*Protein*
16 g	*Total Fat*
1138	*kilojoules (271 Calories)*

Orange Pork Loin Chops

Here's a simple pork chop staple recipe that adds a tangy mustard and Worcestershire sauce. Garnish the serving platter with twists of orange slices to enhance the presentation. See page 145 for a marinade chops recipe.

Pork is usually best cooked to a medium doneness, where the meat will be faintly pink in the centre. If a well doneness is preferred, the pinkness should have disappeared. You will find that bone-in cuts have a more intense pink color near the bone. No health hazard exists because today, in Canada, commercially available pork is virtually trichinosis free.

4	pork loin chops, 2 cm (3/4 inch) thick	4
2 mL	seasoned salt	1/2 tsp
15 mL	vegetable oil	1 tbsp
4	fresh mushrooms, sliced (optional)	4
75 mL	orange juice	1/3 cup
15 mL	Dijon mustard	1 tbsp
2 mL	Worcestershire sauce	1/2 tsp
5 mL	cornstarch	1 tsp

Sprinkle pork with seasoned salt. Heat oil in nonstick skillet over medium-high heat. Brown chops 3 minutes per side. Add mushrooms (if using) and cook 1 minute.

In small bowl, combine orange juice, mustard, Worcestershire sauce and cornstarch; add to skillet.

Worcestershire sauce makes a great marinade to tenderize and enhance the flavour of most meats, particularly beef. Brush on one hour before cooking. Particularly good on barbecued or pan-fried hamburgers.

Reduce heat to low; simmer for 4 minutes, stirring to scrape up brown bits and turning meat after 2 minutes. Serve with sauce.

Makes 4 servings.

FOOD CHOICE VALUE *per serving*

Each Serving: 1/4 of recipe

3 1/2 ☑ *Protein Choices*

1/2 ◰ *Fruits & Vegetables Choice*

1 ▲ *Fats & Oils Choice*

3 g	Carbohydrate
26 g	Protein
16 g	Total Fat
1100	kilojoules (262 Calories)

Pork Schnitzel with Ginger and Julienne Vegetables

This fall classic makes a colorful and tasty dish that's likely to have the family clambering for seconds. It also makes a great presentation when company's expected. Remember not to overcook the pork.

500 g	*pork schnitzel (four – 125 g /4 oz pieces)*	*1 lb*
50 mL	*all-purpose flour*	*1/4 cup*
15 mL	*vegetable oil*	*1 tbsp*
1 mL	*grated gingerroot*	*1/4 tsp*
2	*carrots, julienned*	*2*
Half	*sweet red pepper, julienned*	*Half*
3	*green onions, cut into 8 cm (3 inch) pieces*	*3*
8	*mushrooms, sliced*	*8*
175 mL	*chicken stock*	*3/4 cup*
50 mL	*dry white wine**	*1/4 cup*
5 mL	*lime juice*	*1 tsp*
10 mL	*cornstarch*	*2 tsp*
	Salt and pepper	

Dredge pork in flour. In large nonstick skillet, heat oil over medium-high heat. Cook pork 2 to 2 1/2 minutes per side or until lightly golden. Do not overcook. Transfer to warmed serving platter.

Add ginger, carrots, red pepper, green onions and mushrooms to pan and sauté 3 minutes. Add stock, wine and lime juice; cook 3 to 3 1/2 minutes; or until tender-crisp. With slotted spoon, transfer vegetables to plate with meat.

Dissolve cornstarch in 25 mL (2 tbsp) cold water. Whisk into sauce in skillet. Increase heat to high and cook until thickened slightly. Season with salt and pepper to taste. Drizzle over pork and vegetables.

Makes 4 servings.

*Ask your dietitian or doctor about the use of alcohol.

FOOD CHOICE VALUE per serving

Each Serving: 1/4 of recipe

4	☑	*Protein Choices*
1 1/2	☑	*Fruits & Vegetables Choices*

13 g	*Carbohydrate*
29 g	*Protein*
11 g	*Total Fat*
1150	*kilojoules (274 Calories)*

Marinated Pork Steak

Marinating the meat and being careful not to overcook it ensures succulent results. See page 143 for another good chops recipe.

125 mL	soy sauce*	1/2 cup
125 mL	dry sherry	1/2 cup
125 mL	water	1/2 cup
25 mL	liquid honey	2 tbsp
25 mL	vegetable oil	2 tbsp
2	cloves garlic, minced	2
4	boneless pork steaks or chops (leg or loin), 2.5 to 4 cm (1 to 1 1/2-inches) thick	4

In nonmetallic shallow dish, combine soy sauce, sherry, water, honey, oil and garlic. Add meat and let stand, covered and turning occasionally, at room temperature for 20 to 30 minutes or refrigerated overnight.

Broil 8 to 12 cm (3 to 5 inches) from heat, for 6 to 8 minutes per side or just until no longer pink inside. To barbecue, cook steaks over medium heat 5 to 10 minutes each side.

Makes 4 servings.

Serve with a crusty roll and leafy green salad.

*If concerned about sodium, substitute a low sodium soy sauce.

FOOD CHOICE VALUE *per serving*

Each Serving: 1 Steak/Chop

3 1/2 ☑ Protein Choices

1 g	*Carbohydrate*
27 g	*Protein*
8 g	*Total Fat*
810	*kilojoules (193 Calories)*

Pork Tenderloin with Apricot Sauce

The tangy taste of apricots in this fruity sauce adds zest to tender slices of pork in this easy-to-prepare dish that's sure to have guests ask for the recipe.

375 g	*pork tenderloin*	*3/4 lb*
15 mL	*butter or soft margarine*	*1 tbsp*
15 mL	*finely chopped onion*	*1 tbsp*
125 mL	*no-sugar-added apricot spread*	*1/2 cup*
75 mL	*apricot nectar*	*1/3 cup*
2 mL	*powdered beef bouillon mix*	*1/2 tsp*
	Salt and pepper	

Trim any visible fat from tenderloin; cut crosswise into 4 pieces. Place pieces between sheets of waxed paper and pound to flatten to 5 mm (1/4-inch) thickness.

Melt butter in large nonstick skillet. Brown pork on both sides; remove from pan.

Add onion to pan and sauté until tender. Stir in apricot spread, apricot nectar and bouillon mix.

Return meat to pan; baste with sauce. Bring to boil; reduce heat, cover and simmer 5 to 7 minutes or until meat is no longer pink inside. Remove meat to heated platter; keep warm.

Increase heat to high; cook, stirring until liquid is slightly thickened. Add salt and pepper to taste. Pour over meat.

Makes 4 servings.

FOOD CHOICE VALUE *per serving*

Each Serving: 1/4 of recipe

2	*Protein Choices*
1	*Fruits & Vegetables Choice*
1/2	*Fats & Oils Choice*

8 g	*Carbohydrate*
14 g	*Protein*
8 g	*Total Fat*
685	*kilojoules (163 Calories)*

Roast Loin of Pork Stuffed with Vegetables

This sumptuous main course is great for a special occasion or large family sunday dinners. It takes a little longer to prepare but is guaranteed to be a show-stopper when it arrives at the dinner table.

2	*carrots, julienned*	2
1	*medium zucchini, julienned*	1
1 L	*spinach coarsely chopped*	4 cups
1	*jar (170 mL/6 oz) pimiento*	1
	or roasted red peppers, well drained, julienned	
1	*clove garlic, minced*	1
	Salt and pepper	
2 kg	*double loin pork roast, tied with string*	4 lb
10 mL	*dried thyme*	2 tsp

Bring large pot of water to boil. Add carrots and zucchini; return to boil. Add spinach. Immediately drain and rinse under cold water. Pat vegetables dry. Mix with pimiento and garlic. Season with salt and pepper to taste.

Stuff vegetable mixture into pocket of roast. Season roast with salt, pepper and thyme. Roast on rack in pan in 160°C (350°F) oven for 2 to 2 1/4 hours or until meat thermometer registers 70°C (160°F) basting with pan juices last hour of roasting. Cover with foil and let stand 15 minutes before carving.

Makes 16 servings, each 170g/6 oz.

When roasting, ensure meat thermometer is in center of roast and not touching fat or bone.

Thyme is used to season meat, poultry and fish. Excellent in tomato or cheese dishes. Combine Thyme with melted butter or soft margarine and serve over vegetables or broiled seafood.

FOOD CHOICE VALUE *per serving*

Each Serving: 1/16 of recipe

3 1/2 ☑ *Protein Choices*

1 ➕ *Extra*

2 g	*Carbohydrate*
25 g	*Protein*
11 g	*Total Fat*
903	*kilojoules (215 Calories)*

Mediterranean Pork Kabobs

Brighten up your barbecue with these pork kabobs marinated overnight in garlic,basil and oregano. Serve with a summer fresh salad of garden vegetables.

500 g	*pork loin or leg, cut in 2.5 cm (1 inch) cubes*	*1 lb*
4	*cloves garlic, minced*	*4*
15 mL	*each dried basil and oregano*	*1 tbsp*
	Salt and pepper	
50 mL	*red wine vinegar*	*1/4 cup*
45 mL	*olive oil*	*3 tbsp*
1	*onion, cut in eights*	*1*
2	*sweet peppers, cut in large chunks*	*2*
8	*each cherry tomatoes and mushrooms*	*8*
1	*zucchini, sliced*	*1*

In medium bowl, combine pork, garlic, basil, oregano, salt and pepper to taste, vinegar and oil. Cover and refrigerate to marinate overnight, stirring occasionally.

Alternately thread meat, onion, pepper, tomatoes, mushrooms and zucchini onto skewers. Barbecue 10 cm (4 inches) from heat 4 to 5 minutes per side, brushing with marinade 2 to 3 times during cooking.

Makes 4 servings.

Soak wooden skewers in water for 30 minutes before skewering with meat and vegetables. This prevents them from burning.

GOOD Source of IRON

FOOD CHOICE VALUE *per serving*

Each Serving: 1/4 of recipe

3 1/2 ◪ *Protein Choices*

1 ◲ *Fruits & Vegetables Choice*

1 1/2 ▲ *Fats & Oils Choices*

10 g	*Carbohydrate*
26 g	*Protein*
17 g	*Total Fat*
1231	*kilojoules (293 Calories)*

Pork Pepper Steak

Tender juicy pork drizzled with a wine sauce sprinkled with pepper corns adds a nice zip to these tender pork chops.

15 mL	crushed black peppercorns	1 tbsp
2 mL	dried thyme	1/2 tsp
2 mL	dried tarragon	1/2 tsp
4	butterfly pork loin steaks, cut 2 cm (3/4 inch) thick	4
7 mL	vegetable oil	1 1/2 tsp
7 mL	butter or soft margarine	1 1/2 tsp
25 mL	finely chopped green onions	2 tbsp
125 mL	dry white wine or vermouth*	1/2 cup
50 mL	beef bouillon	1/4 cup

Ask your dietitian or doctor about the use of alcohol.

Combine peppercorns, thyme and tarragon; press firmly into steaks using heel of hand. Let steaks stand 30 minutes at room temperature.

In a non-stick skillet, heat oil and butter over medium heat; cook steaks for 5 to 7 minutes on each side or until juices run clear. Remove and keep warm.

Add onions, wine and bouillon to pan; bring to boil, scraping up brown bits with wooden spoon. Cook until reduced by half. Pour over steaks.

Microwave method: Prepare steaks as in recipe. Heat microwave browning dish at High (100% power) for 6 to 8 minutes. Place steaks in dish; cover and microwave at Medium (50% power) for 5 to 6 minutes on each side or until juices just run clear.

In microwaveable container, microwave onion, wine and bouillon at High (100% power) for 1 1/2 minutes. Combine 10 mL (2 tsp) all-purpose flour with 15 mL (1 tbsp) water; stir into hot mixture. Microwave at High for 1 to 2 minutes, stirring occasionally, until thickened. Serve over steaks.

Makes 4 servings.

FOOD CHOICE VALUE *per serving*

Each Serving: 1/4 of recipe

3 ☑ *Protein Choices*

1 ▲ *Fats & Oils Choice*

2 g	Carbohydrate
23 g	Protein
15 g	Total Fat
1042	kilojoules (248 Calories)

Cajun Breaded Pork

Here's a tasty alternative to packaged spice/coating mixes. Serve with Cajun Cabbage side dish on page 106.

50 mL	*all-purpose flour*	*1/4 cup*
5 mL	*dried thyme*	*1 tsp*
5 mL	*dried sage*	*1 tsp*
2 mL	*garlic powder*	*1/2 tsp*
2 mL	*cayenne pepper*	*1/2 tsp*
1	*egg*	*1*
25 mL	*water*	*2 tbsp*
175 mL	*dry bread crumbs*	*3/4 cup*
250 g	*thinly sliced pork (leg or loin)* *or boneless fast-fry chops (about 8 loin)*	*1/2 lb*
15 mL	*butter*	*1 tbsp*
15 mL	*vegetable oil*	*1 tbsp*

On plate, combine flour, thyme, sage, garlic powder and cayenne. In shallow dish, beat egg with water. Place bread crumbs on third plate. Dredge pork slices in flour; shake off excess. Dip in egg mixture; coat with bread crumbs. (If possible, let dry for up to 30 minutes, to enhance crispness when cooked.)

In heavy skillet, heat butter and oil over medium-high heat; sauté pork until browned, about 1 1/2 minutes on each side. Serve immediately.

Makes 4 servings.

Todays pork is 23% leaner than 10 years ago. This resulted from improved breeding and feeding practices, a revised grading system which rewards pork producers for producing leaner meat; plus better trimming of fat in retail stores.

FOOD CHOICE VALUE *per serving*

Each Serving: 1/4 of recipe

2	▨	*Protein Choices*
1	☐	*Starchy Choice*
1	▲	*Fats & Oils Choice*

12 g	*Carbohydrate*
16 g	*Protein*
11 g	*Total Fat*
907	*kilojoules (216 Calories)*

Fried Rice with Pork and Vegetables

This comforting home-style skillet meal will chase away the winter chills. To save time, cook the rice the night before.

1	*can (540 mL /19 oz)* tomatoes*	*1*
250 mL	*long-grain white rice*	*1 cup*
15 mL	*vegetable oil*	*1 tbsp*
500 g	*boneless pork loin*	*1 lb*
2	*medium carrots, diced*	*2*
1	*medium onion, halved lengthwise and sliced*	*1*
1	*clove garlic, minced*	*1*
7 mL	*dried oregano*	*1 1/2 tsp*
500 mL	*shredded green cabbage*	*2 cups*
25 mL	*soy sauce*	*2 tbsp*
10 mL	*Worcestershire sauce*	*2 tsp*

Drain tomatoes, adding liquid to measuring cup. Add enough water to make 550 mL (2 1/4 cups). Bring liquid to boil in saucepan; stir in rice. Cover and simmer over low heat about 20 minutes or until rice is cooked.

Slice pork across the grain into thin slivers. Heat oil in large skillet over medium-high heat; sauté pork, carrots, onion, garlic and oregano for 5 minutes or until tender.

Reduce heat to low; stir in cooked rice, tomatoes, cabbage, soy sauce and Worcestershire sauce. Heat through, stirring constantly.

Makes 6 servings.

PHOTO ON PAGE 159.

Oregano goes well with any tomato dish. Use to season pasta sauces, pizza, Chili, and stuffings for meat or poultry. When ground, use approx 1/2 tsp to 500g/1 lb ground beef or pork. Use 1/4 tsp leaves in 2 cups tomato, spaghetti or barbecue sauce.

*Recipe has been developed for use with 19 oz or 28 oz can sizes. Nutritional analysis based on 19 oz size only.

HIGH FIBRE

FOOD CHOICE VALUE *per serving*

Each Serving: 1/6 of recipe

2	☑	*Protein Choices*
1 1/2	☐	*Starchy Choices*
1	☑	*Fruits & Vegetables Choice*

33 g	*Carbohydrate*
19 g	*Protein*
7 g	*Total Fat*
1165	*kilojoules (277 Calories)*

MAIN MEALS
CHICKEN/TURKEY

	Microwave	Protein	Starchy	Milk	Fruits & Vegetables	Fats & Oils	Extra	Page
Gourmet Stuffed Chicken		3 1/2	1			1		153
Rosemary Chicken Rolls in Wine		4 1/2			1/2			154
Tandoori Chicken		4		1				155
Lemon Garlic Chicken	•	4			1/2			156
Lemon Glazed Chicken *(Photo: p. 159)*		4			1/2			157
Chicken Parmesan *(Photo: p. 159)*		4			1			158
Chicken Mediterranean *(Photo: p. 161)*	•	4			1			163
Hazelnut Chicken Rolls *(Photo: p. 160)*		4 1/2			1/2	1		164
Szechuan Chicken *(Photo: p. 161)*		2 1/2			1/2			165
Spanish Chicken		4			1/2	2		166
Cajun Country Chicken		4			1 1/2		1	167
Southern-Style Chicken		4	1			1 1/2		168
Chicken Medallions		4						169
Chicken Fettucini		2 1/2	1 1/2	1				170
Chicken with Ginger & Lime	•	4						171
Favorite Turkey Loaf		4	1/2		1/2		1	172
Grecian Turkey Fillet		3 1/2			1			173
Hearty Turkey Bourguignon		2 1/2	1		1 1/2	1/2		174

The Food Choice Values on each recipe do not include accompanying foods which are suggested in many of the recipes and shown in some of the photographs.

Gourmet Stuffed Chicken

Here's a great traditional roast chicken recipe that is enlivened with the savory fruit and nut flavor of the gourmet stuffing. Serve with baked potatoes or rice and a fresh green salad.

1	*roasting chicken (2 to 2.5 kg/4 to 5 lb)*	*1*
	Salt and pepper	
	Poultry seasoning	
75 mL	*dried apricots and prunes, mixed*	*1/3 cup*
250 mL	*strong tea*	*1 cup*
250 mL	*soft whole wheat bread crumbs*	*1 cup*
250 mL	*diced celery*	*1 cup*
125 mL	*chopped walnuts*	*1/2 cup*
50 mL	*chopped fresh parsley*	*1/4 cup*
2 mL	*grated orange rind*	*1/2 tsp*

In saucepan, bring dried fruit mixture and tea to boil; reduce heat and simmer until fruit is tender. Drain and chop. Combine with crumbs, celery, walnuts, parsley and orange rind.

Meanwhile, rinse and dry chicken. Sprinkle cavity with salt, pepper and poultry seasoning; spoon in stuffing. Seal cavity with slice of bread stuffed into opening. Tie legs together.

Roast chicken, uncovered, in 160°C (325°F) oven for 2 to 2 1/2 hours or until leg moves easily in joint and juices run clear when chicken is pierced.

Makes 8 servings, with 750 mL (3 cups) stuffing.

When buying a whole chicken, check the grading tags. A roasting chicken usually requires Grade "A" tags(red tag), while Grade "Utility"(Blue tag) is more economical when serving chicken parts or when the bird will be carved before serving.(A utility bird will have one or more parts missing, such as a wing, drumstick or portion of skin. This can occur during processing.) Roasting chickens weigh 2 to 3 kilos(4 1/2 to 6 1/2 lbs). A smaller "boiler-fryer" chicken is suitable for both moist and dry heat methods of cooking.

Chicken Only

FOOD CHOICE VALUE *per serving*

Each Serving: 1/8 of chicken

3 1/2 ▨ *Protein Choices*

0 g	*Carbohydrate*
25 g	*Protein*
6 g	*Total Fat*
687	*kilojoules (164Calories)*

Stuffing Only

FOOD CHOICE VALUE *per serving*

Each Serving: 125 mL (1/2 cup)

1 ☐ *Starchy Choice*

1 ▲ *Fats & Oils Choice*

13 g	*Carbohydrate*
3 g	*Protein*
7 g	*Total Fat*
483	*kilojoules (115 Calories)*

Rosemary Chicken Rolls in Wine

Chicken breasts take on a new look when filled with a savory stuffing and simmered in white wine.

6	*boneless skinless chicken breasts*	6
1	*egg, beaten*	1
15 mL	*water*	1 tbsp
25 mL	*pine nuts*	2 tbsp
25 mL	*grated Parmesan cheese*	2 tbsp
25 mL	*bread crumbs*	2 tbsp
5 mL	*dried rosemary*	1 tsp
1 mL	*pepper*	1/4 tsp
5 mL	*butter or soft margarine*	1 tbsp
15 mL	*olive oil*	1 tbsp
500 mL	*diced celery*	2 cups
50 mL	*dry white wine**	1/4 cup

Rosemary, a sweet, fragrant herb that resembles the look and scent of pine needles; is excellent in lamb dishes, soups, stews, marinades, poached and broiled fish or sea food. Use in preparing a variety of meats. Sprinkle over coals when barbecuing meats.

*Ask your dietitian or doctor about the use of alcohol.

Place chicken between sheets of waxed paper; pound with mallet until thin. Brush tops with egg mixed with water. Combine nuts, cheese, crumbs, rosemary and pepper; sprinkle evenly over chicken, pressing in with fingers. Roll up from narrow end and fasten with toothpicks.

In skillet, heat butter and olive oil over medium heat; cook chicken rolls about 5 minutes on each side until golden.

Add celery and wine; cover and simmer over low heat for 8 to 10 minutes or until chicken is no longer pink inside. Remove toothpicks.

Makes 6 servings.

FOOD CHOICE VALUE *per serving*

Each Serving: 1/6 of recipe

4 1/2 ☑ *Protein Choices*

1/2 ◪ *Fruits & Vegetables Choice*

4 g	*Carbohydrate*
31 g	*Protein*
10 g	*Total Fat*
991	*kilojoules (236 Calories)*

Tandoori Chicken

A rich blend of Indian spices bring out chicken's own full flavour.
Serve with rice and lentils.

8	*portions chicken*	8
500 mL	*plain low fat yogurt*	*2 cups*
2	*cloves garlic, chopped*	*2*
15 mL	*curry powder*	*1 tbsp*
10 mL	*ground cumin*	*2 tsp*
10 mL	*dried coriander*	*2 tsp*
10 mL	*dried ginger*	*2 tsp*

Cut slits all over chicken. In non-metallic container, combine
yogurt, garlic, curry powder, cumin, coriander and ginger.
Add chicken and turn to coat. Marinate in refrigerator overnight.

Wrap chicken pieces individually in foil. Bake in 180°C
(350°F) oven for 45 minutes or until tender and juices run clear
when chicken is pierced.

Remove chicken from foil and drain. Broil 15 cm (6 inches)
from heat for 2 to 3 minutes or until golden.

Makes 8 servings.

*For even more spice, increase
the cumin, coriander and ginger
by 5 mL (1 tsp) each.*

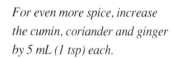

FOOD CHOICE VALUE *per serving*

Each Serving: 1/8 of recipe

4 ☑ *Protein Choices*

1 ◆ *Milk Choice (2%)*

6 g	*Carbohydrate*
31 g	*Protein*
15 g	*Total Fat*
1214	*kilojoules (289 Calories)*

Lemon Garlic Chicken

A very simple tart and fragrant combination of seasonings complements this chicken's own delicious taste.

4	*boneless skinless chicken breasts*	*4*
1	*lemon, cut in half*	*1*
1	*clove garlic, finely minced*	*1*
25 mL	*minced fresh parsley*	*2 tbsp*
2 mL	*dried oregano*	*1/2 tsp*

Arrange chicken breasts in single layer in round microwaveable dish. Sprinkle with juice of half a lemon. Cut other half (with peel) into thin slices; arrange over chicken.

Cover and microwave at High (100% power) for 5 minutes or until chicken is no longer pink inside, rotating once during cooking. Let stand 2 minutes before serving.

Makes 4 servings.

Uncooked chicken (whole and pieces) may be safely stored in the refrigerator (4°C, 40°F) for 2 to 3 days. Cooked chicken is good for 3 to 4 days. Uncooked chicken pieces may be frozen (-18°C, 0°F) for 6 months (Whole for 8 months). Cooked chicken should only be frozen for 1 to 3 months. Never re-freeze thawed, uncooked chicken. When chicken is thawed, keep refrigerated and cook within 48 hours.

FOOD CHOICE VALUE	*per serving*
Each Serving: 1/4 of recipe	
4	☑ *Protein Choices*
1	➕ *Extra*

3 g	*Carbohydrate*
27 g	*Protein*
3 g	*Total Fat*
624	*kilojoules (150 Calories)*

Lemon Glazed Chicken

PHOTO ON PAGE 159.

This succulent piquant chicken will be on the table in no time. Accompany it with crisp fresh salad and parsleyed new potatoes.

4	*boneless, skinless chicken breasts, slightly flattened*	4
	All-purpose flour	
50 mL	*butter*	*3 tbsp*
50 mL	*water*	*3 tbsp*
15 mL	*lemon juice*	*1 tbsp*
7 mL	*chicken bouillon mix*	*1 1/2 tsp*
	Chopped fresh parsley	
	Lemon slices	

Coat chicken in small amount of flour; shake off excess. In nonstick skillet, melt butter; sauté chicken on each side until lightly browned.

Add water, lemon juice and chicken bouillon mix to pan; stir until dissolved. Bring to a boil; cover and simmer 5 to 7 minutes or until chicken is no longer pink inside. Remove chicken to serving plate; keep warm.

Cook and stir pan juices over high heat until thickened and syrupy, 1 to 2 minutes. Pour glaze over chicken. Garnish with parsley and lemon slices.

Makes 4 servings.

FOOD CHOICE VALUE *per serving*

Each Serving: 1 chicken breast

4 ☑ *Protein Choices*

1/2 ◨ *Fruits & Vegetables Choice*

4 g	Carbohydrate
28 g	Protein
11 g	Total Fat
974	kilojoules (232 Calories)

Chicken Parmesan

The original Italian recipe gets a little zip from the hot pepper sauce. Buon Appetito! Serve over cooked pasta, if desired.

15 mL	*vegetable oil*	*1 tbsp*
4	*boneless skinless chicken breasts*	*4*
20 mL	*cornstarch*	*4 tsp*
1	*can (540 mL / 19 oz)* stewed tomatoes*	*1*
2 mL	*dried oregano*	*1/2 tsp*
2 mL	*dried basil*	*1/2 tsp*
1 mL	*hot pepper sauce*	*1/4 tsp*
50 mL	*grated Parmesan cheese*	*1/4 cup*

Heat oil in skillet over medium-high heat; brown chicken on both sides.

Dissolve cornstarch in tomatoes; add to pan along with oregano, basil and hot pepper sauce. Simmer over low heat, stirring occasionally, until chicken is tender, 10 to 15 minutes. Sprinkle with cheese.

Brown lightly under broiler 2 to 3 minutes, protecting handle with foil if necessary.

Makes 4 servings.

PHOTO ON PAGE 159.

Oregano goes well with any tomato dish. Use to season pasta sauces, pizza, Chili, and stuffings for meat or poultry. When ground, use approx 1/2 tsp to 500g/1 lb ground beef or pork. Use 1/4 tsp leaves in 2 cups tomato, spaghetti or barbecue sauce.

*Recipe has been developed for use with 19 oz or 28 oz can sizes. Nutritional analysis based on 19 oz size only.

FOOD CHOICE VALUE *per serving*

Each Serving: 1/4 of recipe

4	☑ *Protein Choices*
1	◨ *Fruits & Vegetables Choice*

13 g	*Carbohydrate*
31 g	*Protein*
7 g	*Total Fat*
995	*kilojoules (237 Calories)*

Lemon Glazed Chicken (p.157)

Chicken Parmesan (p.158)

Fried Rice with Pork & Vegetables (p.151)

159

Hazelnut Chicken Rolls (p.164)

Chicken Mediterranean (p.163)

Szechuan Chicken (p.165)

161

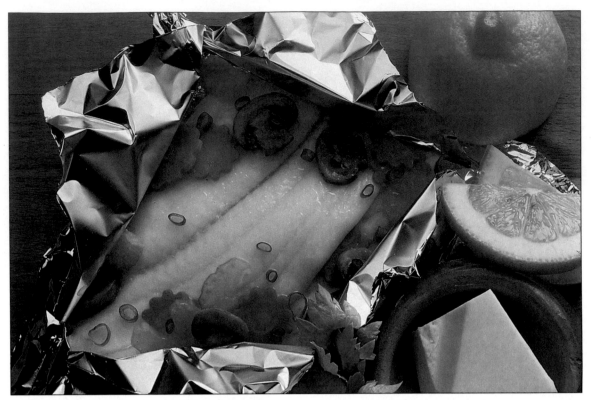

***Fish Baked In Foil** (p.177)*

***Dilly Cucumber Fish** (p.176)*

***New Orleans Fish Creole** (p.179)*

162

Chicken Mediterranean

PHOTO ON PAGE 161.

To make chicken mediterranean for a crowd, double the recipe, cover and bake in 190°C (375°F) oven for 50 minutes, basting once during baking. Then uncover and bake 10 minutes longer.

This Mediterranean-style dish becomes a meal in itself when served on rice.

4	*boneless skinless chicken breasts*	4
1	*medium zucchini*	1
Half	*small eggplant*	Half
3	*plum tomatoes*	3
Half	*large onion*	Half
1 to 2	*cloves garlic, finely minced*	1 to 2
5 mL	*dried basil*	1 tsp
2 mL	*dried oregano*	1/2 tsp
2 mL	*dried marjoram*	1/2 tsp
Pinch	*pepper*	Pinch

Arrange chicken breasts in single layer in round microwaveable dish.

Chop zucchini, eggplant, tomatoes and onion coarsely; sprinkle evenly over chicken. Combine garlic, basil, oregano, marjoram and pepper; sprinkle evenly over vegetables.

Cover and microwave at High (100% power) for 15 to 20 minutes or until chicken is no longer pink inside, rotating once during cooking. Let stand 3 minutes before serving.

Conventional Cooking Method: In a baking pan, prepare chicken and vegetables as described above. Cover and bake at 190°C (375°F) for 50 minutes, basting once during baking. Uncover and bake about 10 minutes longer, or until chicken and vegetables are tender, basting several times.

Makes 4 servings.

FOOD CHOICE VALUE *per serving*

Each Serving: 1/4 of recipe

4	☑ *Protein Choices*
1	☐ *Fruits & Vegetables Choice*

8 g	*Carbohydrate*
28 g	*Protein*
3 g	*Total Fat*
745	*kilojoules (178 Calories)*

Hazelnut Chicken Rolls

Roll up a terrific combination of taste sensations – crunchy hazelnuts, tender chicken and a spinach and cheese stuffing.

6	*boneless skinless chicken breasts*	6
1	*pkg (300 g) frozen chopped spinach, cooked and pressed dry*	1
25 mL	*grated Parmesan cheese*	2 tbsp
1	*egg, beaten*	1
125 mL	*hazelnuts, finely chopped*	1/2 cup
50 mL	*whole wheat flour*	1/4 cup
1 mL	*pepper*	1/4 tsp
15 mL	*butter or soft margarine*	1 tbsp
25 mL	*olive oil*	2 tbsp
50 mL	*dry white wine**	1/4 cup

Place chicken between sheets of waxed paper; pound with mallet until thin. Spoon some spinach and 5 mL (1 tsp) Parmesan cheese evenly onto each chicken breast. Roll up from narrow end; fasten with toothpick.

In shallow dish, combine hazelnuts, flour and pepper. Dip rolls into beaten egg, then nut mixture.

In baking dish, heat butter and olive oil; place rolls in pan and bake in 190°C (375°F) oven for 45 minutes. Remove rolls to heated platter; remove toothpick. Add wine to pan and stir to loosen any browned bits. Pour over chicken.

Makes 6 servings.

PHOTO ON PAGE 160.

*Ask your dietitian or doctor about the use of alcohol.

FOOD CHOICE VALUE	*per serving*
Each Serving: 1/6 of recipe	
4 1/2 ☑ *Protein Choices*	
1/2 ◩ *Fruits & Vegetables Choice*	
1 ◣ *Fats & Oils Choice*	

7 g	*Carbohydrate*
32 g	*Protein*
18 g	*Total Fat*
1331	*kilojoules (317 Calories)*

Szechuan Chicken

PHOTO ON PAGE 161.

Ready in minutes, these spicy strips will really please those who like it hot, since you can add the hot pepper to your liking. Serve with rice or soft Chinese noodles.

500 g	boneless skinless chicken breasts	1 lb
25 mL	peanut oil	2 tbsp
15 mL	grated orange rind	1 tbsp
5 to 10 mL	grated gingerroot	1 to 2 tsp
2	cloves garlic, minced	2
	Hot pepper flakes	
50 mL	orange juice	1/4 cup
15 mL	vinegar	1 tbsp
15 mL	soy sauce	1 tbsp
25 mL	orange juice	2 tbsp
10 mL	cornstarch	2 tsp

Cut chicken into 1 cm (1/2-inch) strips.

Heat oil in large skillet over medium heat; sauté orange rind, ginger, garlic, and hot pepper flakes to taste for 5 minutes.

Add 50 mL (1/4 cup) orange juice, vinegar, soy sauce and chicken; bring to boil. Reduce heat and simmer for 10 minutes. Dissolve cornstarch in 25 mL (2 tbsp) orange juice; add to pan and cook, stirring, until thickened.

Makes 6 servings.

FOOD CHOICE VALUE *per serving*

Each Serving: 1/6 of recipe

2 1/2 ☑ *Protein Choices*

1/2 ☐ *Fruits & Vegetables Choice*

3 g	Carbohydrate
18 g	Protein
7 g	Total Fat
622	kilojoules (148 Calories)

Spanish Chicken

You can almost taste the sun in this colorful and flavorful dish.
Particularly nice in late summer when garden tomatoes are ripe
and juicy

8	*portions chicken*	*8*
25 mL	*olive oil*	*2 tbsp*
15 mL	*butter or soft margarine*	*1 tbsp*
1	*medium onion, cut in wedges*	*1*
2	*cloves garlic, chopped*	*2*
3	*carrots, sliced*	*3*
50 mL	*chopped fresh parsley*	*1/4 cup*
2	*bay leaves*	*2*
50 mL	*dry white wine* or chicken broth*	*1/4 cup*
50 mL	*pitted black olives, chopped*	*1/4 cup*
50 mL	*pine nuts*	*1/4 cup*
2	*firm tomatoes, diced*	*2*

In skillet, heat oil and butter over medium heat; cook chicken until
well browned. Remove chicken. Add onion and garlic to pan; sauté
until translucent.

Return chicken to pan along with carrots, parsley, bay leaves and
wine. Cover and simmer for 30 minutes or until juices run clear
when chicken is pierced. Remove bay leaves.

Add olives, pine nuts and tomatoes; simmer a few more minutes
until heated through. With slotted spoon, transfer chicken and
vegetables to platter. Serve extra liquid separately as sauce.

Makes 8 servings.

**Ask your dietitian or doctor
about the use of alcohol.*

FOOD CHOICE VALUE *per serving*

Each Serving: 1/8 of recipe

4	☑	*Protein Choices*
1/2	◼	*Fruits & Vegetables Choice*
2	▲	*Fats & Oils Choices*

6 g	*Carbohydrate*
29 g	*Protein*
21 g	*Total Fat*
1407	*kilojoules (335 Calories)*

Cajun Country Chicken

Curry and thyme spice up this tomato based southern dish with a delicate blend of flavour and aromas. Serve this New Orleans specialty over a bed of steaming rice or egg noodles.

Slivering chicken hastens cooking time. A large skillet helps evaporation of liquid to thicken the sauce faster.

*Recipe has been developed for use with 19 oz or 28 oz can sizes. Nutritional analysis based on 19 oz size only.

25 mL	cornstarch	2 tbsp
5 mL	curry powder	1 tsp
2 mL	dried thyme	1/2 tsp
500 g	boneless skinless chicken breasts, cut in thin strips	1 lb
25 mL	vegetable oil	2 tbsp
1	sweet green pepper, slivered	1
1	medium onion, sliced	1
1	can (540 mL / 19 oz)* stewed tomatoes	1

Combine cornstarch, curry powder and thyme; dredge chicken in mixture.

Heat half of the oil in large skillet over medium-high heat. Sauté green pepper and onion for 3 minutes or until tender. Remove from pan. Add remaining oil to pan; sauté chicken for 2 minutes.

Return vegetables to pan along with tomatoes. Bring to boil; simmer, uncovered, for 10 to 15 minutes or until slightly thickened and chicken is tender.

Makes 4 servings, each 280 g/10 oz.

FOOD CHOICE VALUE *per serving*

Each Serving: 1/4 of recipe

4	☑ *Protein Choices*
1 1/2	◪ *Fruits & Vegetables Choices*
1	✚ *Extra*

16 g	*Carbohydrate*
27 g	*Protein*
10 g	*Total Fat*
1100	*kilojoules* (262 Calories)

Southern-Style Chicken

Here's what you've been waiting for: Southern-fried crispiness
and taste without the deep-frying.

6	*portions chicken*	6
175 mL	*whole wheat flour*	*3/4 cup*
15 mL	*wheat bran*	*1 tbsp*
10 mL	*paprika*	*2 tsp*
5 mL	*poultry seasoning*	*1 tsp*
2 mL	*allspice*	*1/2 tsp*
2 mL	*garlic powder*	*1/2 tsp*
2 mL	*salt*	*1/2 tsp*
2 mL	*pepper*	*1/2 tsp*
1	*egg, beaten*	*1*
15 mL	*milk*	*1 tbsp*
10	*drops hot pepper sauce*	*10*
25 mL	*olive oil*	*2 tbsp*

In shallow dish, combine flour, bran, paprika, poultry seasoning,
allspice, garlic, salt and pepper. In separate shallow dish, beat
together egg, milk and hot pepper sauce.

Dip chicken pieces into egg mixture, then into flour mixture, coating
well. Place in well-greased roasting pan; drizzle with oil. Bake in
190°C (375°F) oven for 50 to 60 minutes, basting occasionally, until
tender and juices run clear when chicken is pierced.

Makes 6 servings.

FOOD CHOICE VALUE	*per serving*
Each Serving: 1/6 of recipe	
4	☑ *Protein Choices*
1	☐ *Starchy Choice*
1 1/2	▲ *Fats & Oils Choices*

12 g	*Carbohydrate*
31 g	*Protein*
20 g	*Total Fat*
1457	*kilojoules (347 Calories)*

Chicken Medallions

Regular chicken breasts are transformed into gourmet bite-size morsels when flattened and spiced with this delicate blend of basil, garlic and wine.

Basil is sometimes called the "tomato herb" and may be used in most Tomato recipes. Basil blends well with other herbs in seasoning foods. Suggested amounts to use: -1/4 to 1/2 tsp in 2 cups green vegetables. -3/4 to 1 1/2 tsp for 1 1/2 lbs pork chops or roasts.

500 g	*boneless skinless chicken breasts*	*1 lb*
10 mL	*dried basil*	*2 tsp*
5 mL	*garlic powder*	*1 tsp*
1 mL	*pepper*	*1/4 tsp*
15 mL	*butter or soft margarine*	*1 tbsp*
15 mL	*olive oil*	*1 tbsp*
50 mL	*white wine**	*1/4 cup*

Place chicken between sheets of waxed paper; pound with mallet until thin. Combine basil, garlic and pepper; sprinkle evenly over chicken, pressing in with fingers. Cut into medallion-sized pieces.

In skillet, heat butter and oil over medium heat; cook medallions 5 minutes on each side. Remove to warm platter.

Add wine to skillet and stir to loosen any browned bits. Pour over medallions.

Makes 4 servings

*Ask your dietitian or doctor about the use of alcohol.

FOOD CHOICE VALUE *per serving*

Each Serving: 1/4 of recipe

4 ☑ *Protein Choices*

---

1 g	*Carbohydrate*
27 g	*Protein*
9 g	*Total Fat*
865	*kilojoules (206 Calories)*

Chicken Fettuccine

The uniquely rich taste of this sauce offers a new dimention to traditional fettucini-without the typical rich calories of cream sauces. Serve with a baguette of garlic bread.

250 mL	*chicken broth*	*1 cup*
250 mL	*tomato juice*	*1 cup*
50 mL	*all-purpose flour*	*1/4 cup*
1 mL	*nutmeg*	*1/4 tsp*
Pinch	*pepper*	*Pinch*
500 mL	*coarsely chopped cooked chicken*	*2 cups*
3	*carrots, coarsely grated*	*3*
350g	*spinach noodles*	*12 1/2 oz*
75 mL	*grated Parmesan cheese*	*1/3 cup*

In large saucepan, combine chicken broth, tomato juice, flour, nutmeg and pepper; heat over medium heat, stirring frequently, until thickened.

Add chicken and carrots; simmer until heated through.

Meanwhile, cook spinach noodles according to manufacturer's directions. Drain and arrange on heated platter. Pour chicken mixture over noodles. Sprinkle with Parmesan cheese.

Makes 6 servings.

FOOD CHOICE VALUE *per serving*

Each Serving: 1/6 of recipe

2 1/2 ☑ *Protein Choices*

1 1/2 ☐ *Starchy Choices*

1 ☑ *Fruits & Vegetables Choice*

31 g	*Carbohydrate*
21 g	*Protein*
9 g	*Total Fat*
1231	*kilojoules (293 Calories)*

Chicken with Ginger and Lime

Two of the Caribbean's favorite ingredients get together to prove that chicken goes everywhere in style.

4	*boneless skinless chicken breasts*	4
15 to 25 mL	*fresh fennel leaves*	*1 to 2 tbsp*
15 mL	*grated gingerroot*	*1 tbsp*
25 mL	*lime juice*	*2 tbsp*
Pinch	*pepper*	*Pinch*

Arrange chicken breasts in single layer in round microwaveable dish. Sprinkle with fennel leaves, ginger, and lime juice.

Cover and microwave at High (100% power) for about 5 minutes or until chicken is no longer pink inside. Let stand 2 minutes before serving.

Makes 4 servings.

FOOD CHOICE VALUE *per serving*

Each Serving: 1/4 of recipe

4   ☑ *Protein Choices*

1 g	*Carbohydrate*
27 g	*Protein*
3 g	*Total Fat*
613	*kilojoules (146 Calories)*

Favorite Turkey Loaf

Instead of plain old meat loaf, try this ground turkey variation with
a bread crumb topping. Serve with fluffy mashed potatoes and green
beans. Makes for great meatloaf sandwiches the day after.

1 kg	*ground turkey*	*2 lb*
1	*medium onion, finely chopped*	*1*
1	*sweet green pepper, diced*	*1*
2	*carrots, shredded*	*2*
2	*eggs, lightly beaten*	*2*
125 mL	*tomato paste*	*1/2 cup*
175 mL	*dried bread crumbs*	*3/4 cup*
2 mL	*salt*	*1/2 tsp*
5 mL	*dried oregano*	*1 tsp*
5 mL	*Worcestershire sauce*	*1 tsp*

TOPPING

25 mL	*dried bread crumbs*	*2 tbsp*
10 mL	*chopped fresh parsley*	*2 tsp*

In bowl, combine turkey, onion, green pepper, carrots, eggs, tomato
paste, bread crumbs, salt, oregano and Worcestershire sauce; mix
well and shape into loaf. Place in loaf pan.

Topping: Toss bread crumbs with parsley; sprinkle over loaf. Bake in
180°C (350°F) oven for 1 hour or until meat thermometer registers
85°C (185°F).

Makes 8 servings, each 170 g/6 oz.

FOOD CHOICE VALUE	per serving
Each Serving: 1/8 of recipe	
4	*Protein Choices*
1/2	*Starchy Choice*
1/2	*Fruits & Vegetables Choice*
1	*Exrta*
14 g	*Carbohydrate*
31 g	*Protein*
7 g	*Total Fat*
1033	*kilojoules (246 Calories)*

Grecian Turkey Fillet

Everyone will gobble-gobble these tender fillets. The simmered flavors of garlic, chopped tomatoes and black olives give this simple dish a distinctive Mediterranean flair.

4	*turkey fillets (100 g/3 oz) each*	4
10 mL	*vegetable oil*	2 tsp
25 mL	*dried bread crumbs*	2 tbsp
	Paprika	
15 mL	*vegetable oil*	1 tbsp
1	*clove garlic, minced*	1
4	*medium tomatoes, peeled, seeded and coarsely chopped*	4
4	*green onions, sliced*	4
2 mL	*crushed dried oregano*	1/2 tsp
10 mL	*dry white wine*	2 tsp
25 mL	*chopped fresh parsley*	2 tbsp
10 mL	*chopped black olives*	2 tsp
	Lemon twists	

In baking dish, brush turkey fillets with 10 mL (2 tsp) vegetable oil. Sprinkle with bread crumbs, and paprika to taste. Bake in 180°C (350°F) oven 30 minutes.

Heat 15 mL (1 tbsp) vegetable oil in skillet. Add garlic and sauté lightly. Add tomatoes, green onions, oregano and wine; bring to boil. Reduce heat and simmer 3 minutes.

Place turkey fillets on serving plates and spoon tomato sauce over turkey. Top with chopped parsley and black olives. Garnish with lemon twists.

Makes 4 servings, each 200 g/7 oz.

GOOD Source of IRON

FOOD CHOICE VALUE *per serving*

Each Serving: 1/4 of recipe

3 1/2 ☑ *Protein Choices*

1 ☐ *Fruits & Vegetables Choice*

9 g	*Carbohydrate*
26 g	*Protein*
7 g	*Total Fat*
836	*kilojoules (199 Calories)*

Hearty Turkey Bourguignon

A rich, savory stew that uses refrigerated crescent rolls to
form a top crust.

1 kg	turkey thighs, boned, skinned and cut into 1 cm (1/2-inch) cubes	2 lb
50 mL	all-purpose flour	1/4 cup
25 mL	vegetable oil	2 tbsp
125 mL	dry red wine*	1/2 cup
1	can (398 mL/14 oz) tomato sauce	1
2 mL	dried thyme	1/2 tsp
3	cloves garlic, minced	3
250 mL	small pearl onions (or 1 large onion, chopped)	1 cup
250 mL	frozen peas	1 cup
1	pkg (235 g) refrigerator crescent rolls	1
	Salt and pepper to taste	

Coat turkey in flour. In medium skillet, heat oil; add turkey and sauté
5 minutes until evenly browned. Transfer to 3 L (9 x 13 inch) glass
baking dish.

To skillet, add wine, tomato sauce, thyme and garlic; mix well.
Bring to boil, stirring and scraping up bits from bottom of pan.

Pour tomato sauce mixture over turkey. Add onions, cover and bake
in 180°C (350°F) oven for 1 1/2 hours. Add peas; cover and bake
5 minutes longer.

Separate and roll crescent dough according to package directions.
Arrange crescents on hot casserole. Return to oven and bake,
uncovered, 12 to 15 minutes until rolls are golden.

Makes 6 servings.

*Ask your dietitian or doctor
about the use of alcohol.*

FOOD CHOICE VALUE *per serving*

Each Serving: 1/6 of recipe

2 1/2	Protein Choices
1	Starchy Choice
1 1/2	Fruits & Vegetables Choices
1/2	Fats & Oils Choice
35 g	Carbohydrate
20 g	Protein
9 g	Total Fat
1311	kilojoules (313 Calories)

MAIN MEALS

FISH & SEAFOOD

	 Microwave	Protein	Starchy	Fruits & Vegetables	Fats & Oils	Extra	Page
Dilly Cucumber Fish *(Photo: p. 162)*		3			2		176
Fish Baked in Foil *(Photo: p. 162)*		3		1/2			177
Louisiana-Style Fish	●	2 1/2	2	1/2			178
New Orleans Fish Creole *(Photo: p. 162)*	●	3		1 1/2		1	179
Salmon & Potato Casserole		2	2				180
Fresh Trout Wraps	●	4		1/2			181
Tuna Frittata		3 1/2		1	2		182
Basil-Pepper Sole	●	4	1	1			183
Seafood Stew	●	4 1/2		2			184
Neptune Chicken	●	4	1/2				185

The Food Choice Values on each recipe do not include accompanying foods which are suggested in many of the recipes and shown in some of the photographs.

Dilly Cucumber Fish

Whether you prefer haddock, halibut, bluefish or cod, they will all be highlighted by the lemony dill butter.

1	*small cucumber, thinly sliced*	*1*
500 g	*white fish fillets (thawed if frozen)*	*1 lb*
	Lemon juice	
	Salt	
	Lemon Dill Butter*	

Place overlapping cucumber slices in centre of large piece of foil. Pat fish dry; arrange in single layer on top of cucumber. Sprinkle with lemon juice and salt to taste. Bring edges of foil together; fold to seal. Place on baking sheet. Bake in 230°C (450°F) oven for 10 minutes or until fish flakes easily with fork. Drain fish and cucumber. Serve with Lemon Dill Butter.

Makes 4 servings, each 140 g/5 oz.

PHOTO ON PAGE 162.

*Lemon Dill Butter: Cream together 45 mL (3 tbsp) softened butter, 10 mL (2 tsp) lemon juice, 2 mL (1/2 tsp) dried dillweed (or your favorite herb) and pinch of salt.

If not using Dill Butter, remove 2 Fats & Oils Choices from analysis below, ie. 3 Protein Choices only.

FOOD CHOICE VALUE	*per serving*
Each Serving: 1/4 of recipe	
3	☑ *Protein Choices*
2	▲ *Fats & Oils Choices*

1 g	*Carbohydrate*
22 g	*Protein*
10 g	*Total Fat*
763	*kilojoules (182 Calories)*

Fish Baked in Foil

PHOTO ON PAGE 162.

If you wish, serve this meal-in-a-packet dish right in its wrappings by cutting an "X" in the tops with scissors.

25 mL	*butter*	2 tbsp
25 mL	*sliced green onions*	2 tbsp
500 mL	*thinly sliced fresh mushrooms*	2 cups
250 mL	*thinly sliced carrots*	1 cup
250 mL	*thinly sliced celery*	1 cup
	Seasoned salt	
500 g	*fresh or thawed frozen fish fillets*	1 lb
20 mL	*lemon juice*	4 tsp

In large frypan, melt butter; sauté onions, mushrooms, carrots and celery until tender-crisp and any liquid has evaporated. Add seasoned salt to taste.

Cut foil into four 30 cm (4 inch) squares. Divide vegetable mixture among squares, placing near middle of each square; top with fish. Sprinkle lemon juice evenly over each serving. Fold half of foil over to form triangle; seal edges.

Place packages on baking sheet. Bake in 180°C (350°F) oven 15 minutes or until fish flakes easily when tested with fork.

Makes 4 servings.

FOOD CHOICE VALUE *per serving*

Each Serving: 1/4 of recipe

3 ☑ *Protein Choices*

1/2 ☐ *Fruits & Vegetables Choice*

5 g	*Carbohydrate*
21 g	*Protein*
6 g	*Total Fat*
689	*kilojoules (164 Calories)*

Louisiana-Style Fish

Quick-cooking rice simmers with fish and tomatoes to provide a meal-in-a-pan. Just add a salad and dinner is ready.

25 mL	*butter or soft margarine*	*2 tbsp*
1	*medium onion, chopped*	*1*
1	*clove garlic, minced*	*1*
125 mL	*finely chopped celery*	*1/2 cup*
1	*can (540 mL / 19 oz)* stewed tomatoes*	*1*
2 mL	*dried oregano*	*1/2 tsp*
2 mL	*dried marjoram*	*1/2 tsp*
300 mL	*quick-cooking rice*	*1 1/4 cups*
1	*pkg (400 g) individually frozen fish fillets*	*1*

Any fish can be used, but individually frozen fish fillets cook faster than a frozen block and there is no need to thaw before cooking.

*Recipe has been developed for use with 19 oz or 28 oz can sizes. Nutritional analysis based on 19 oz size only.

Conventional method: In large skillet, melt butter over medium heat. Sauté onion, garlic and celery for 3 minutes or until tender. Stir in tomatoes, oregano and marjoram; bring to boil.

Stir in rice; place fish fillets on top. Cover and simmer over low heat for 12 to 15 minutes or until fish flakes with fork.

Microwave method: In shallow 3 L (12 cup) microwaveable casserole, combine butter, onion, garlic and celery; cover and microwave at High (100% power) 4 minutes or until tender.

Stir in tomatoes, oregano and marjoram; cover and microwave at High 3 to 4 minutes or until mixture comes to boil. Stir in rice and top with fish. Cover and microwave at High 8 to 9 minutes or until fish flakes easily when tested with fork, rotating dish once.

Makes 4 servings, each 300 g/11 oz.

FOOD CHOICE VALUE *per serving*

Each Serving: 1/4 of recipe

2 1/2	✓	*Protein Choices*
2	☐	*Starchy Choices*
1/2	✓	*Fruits & Vegetables Choice*

35 g	*Carbohydrate*
23 g	*Protein*
7 g	*Total Fat*
1230	*kilojoules (293 Calories)*

New Orleans Fish Creole

Seafood lovers will be suitably impressed by this tomato based Southern classic which boasts easy preparation. Use this recipe for those "can't decide what to eat" evenings, by always keeping a can of stewed tomatoes in the pantry and frozen fillets in the freezer.

15 mL	*vegetable oil*	*1 tbsp*
1	*onion, chopped*	*1*
1	*sweet green pepper, chopped*	*1*
1	*carrot, chopped*	*1*
2 mL	*dried oregano*	*1/2 tsp*
25 mL	*all-purpose flour*	*2 tbsp*
1	*can (540 mL/19 oz)* stewed tomatoes*	*1*
5 mL	*Worcestershire sauce*	*1 tsp*
500 g	*white fish fillets, fresh or frozen (thawed)*	*1 lb*

Conventional method: In large skillet, heat oil over medium heat; sauté onion, green pepper, carrot and oregano for 5 minutes. Stir in flour. Add tomatoes and Worcestershire sauce; bring to boil.

Place fish on top of tomato mixture; cover and simmer over low heat 10 to 15 minutes or until fish flakes easily when tested with fork.

Microwave method: Combine oil, onion, green pepper, carrot and oregano in 2.5 L (10-cup) microwaveable round shallow casserole. Cover and microwave at High (100% power) 3 minutes. Stir in flour.

Add tomatoes and Worcestershire sauce; cover and microwave at High 5 to 7 minutes or until boiling. Add fish, cover and microwave at High 5 to 8 minutes or until fish flakes easily when tested with fork.

Makes 4 servings, each 300 g/11oz.

PHOTO ON PAGE 162.

MICROWAVEABLE

Although you can use any firm-fleshed white fish in this creole, haddock makes it outstanding.

*Recipe has been developed for use with 19 oz or 28 oz can sizes. Nutritional analysis based on 19 oz size only.

FOOD CHOICE VALUE *per serving*

Each Serving : 1/4 of recipe

3	☑	*Protein Choices*
1 1/2	◪	*Fruits & Vegetables Choices*
1	⊞	*Extra*

17 g	*Carbohydrate*
23 g	*Protein*
4 g	*Total Fat*
832	*kilojoules (198 Calories)*

Salmon and Potato Casserole

You can put this easy-to-make dish together in about 15 minutes if you cook the potatoes in a microwave. Serve with a tomato salad and a green vegetable.

3	large baking potatoes, cooked and sliced	3
50 mL	chopped green onions	1/4 cup
125 mL	chopped fresh parsley	1/2 cup
1	can (213 g/7.5 oz) salmon or tuna, drained	1
1	egg	1
3	egg whites	3
150 mL	skim milk	2/3 cup
250 mL	shredded part-skim mozzarella cheese	1 cup
	Salt, black pepper and cayenne	
	TOPPING	
50 mL	fresh bread crumbs	1/4 cup
15 mL	grated Parmesan cheese	1 tbsp

In shallow greased 2 L (8 cup) baking dish, arrange layers of half the potatoes, green onions and parsley. Arrange salmon over top. Cover with remaining potatoes, onions and parsley.

Lightly beat egg and egg whites; add milk, cheese, and salt, pepper and cayenne to taste; pour over potatoes.

Topping: Combine bread crumbs and cheese; sprinkle over top. Bake, uncovered, in 180°C (350°F) oven for 25 to 30 minutes or until heated through and set.

Makes 6 servings.

FOOD CHOICE VALUE		*per serving*
Each Serving: 1/6 of recipe		
2	☑ *Protein Choices*	
2	☐ *Starchy Choices*	
28 g	*Carbohydrate*	
18 g	*Protein*	
6 g	*Total Fat*	
1016	*kilojoules (242 Calories)*	

Fresh Trout Wraps

You'll be awash in compliments this summer when you serve your family angler these fresh from the garden tomato,cucumber & dill stuffed fillets. Could also be served cold with yogurt and fresh cucumber slices.

4	*trout, filleted and skinned (each about 125 g / 1/4 lb)*	*4*
2 mL	*each salt and pepper*	*1/2 tsp*
125 mL	*coarsely chopped English cucumber*	*1/2 cup*
125 mL	*coarsely chopped tomato*	*1/2 cup*
50 mL	*fine bread crumbs*	*1/4 cup*
25 mL	*finely chopped onion*	*2 tbsp*
15 mL	*chopped fresh dill*	*1 tbsp*
	(5 mL / 1 tsp dried dillweed)	
10 mL	*lemon juice*	*2 tsp*

Pat fillets dry. Sprinkle with salt and pepper.

Combine cucumber, tomato, bread crumbs, onion, dill and lemon juice; divide among fillets. Roll up and secure with toothpick.

Conventional method: Place fillets, filling side up, in small baking dish; bake, uncovered, in 200°C (400°F) oven for 25 minutes.

Microwave method: Cover fish with vented plastic wrap. Microwave at High (100% power) 4 minutes. Let stand, covered, 5 minutes.

Makes 4 servings.

MICROWAVEABLE

FOOD CHOICE VALUE *per serving*

Each Serving: 1/4 of recipe

4 ▨ *Protein Choices*

1/2 ▢ *Fruits & Vegetables Choice*

6 g	*Carbohydrate*
27 g	*Protein*
8 g	*Total Fat*
848	*kilojoules (202 Calories)*

Tuna Frittata

Originally from Spain, frittatas make light meals to satisfy the heartiest appetites.

25 mL	*butter or soft margarine*	*1 tbsp*
1	*small onion, chopped*	*1*
1	*stalk celery, chopped*	*1*
3	*eggs*	*3*
50 mL	*milk*	*1/4 cup*
1 mL	*salt*	*1/4 tsp*
Pinch	*pepper*	*Pinch*
125 mL	*frozen peas, thawed*	*1/2 cup*
1	*can (85 g/3 oz) tuna, drained and flaked*	*1*
15 mL	*grated Parmesan cheese*	*1 tbsp*

In two 15 cm (6 inch) or one 25 cm (10 inch) ovenproof skillet, melt butter over medium heat. Sauté onion and celery for 3 minutes.

Whisk together eggs, milk, salt and pepper. Stir in peas and tuna. Pour into skillet. Bake in 180°C (350°F) oven for 4 minutes. Sprinkle with cheese. Bake 3 to 4 minutes longer or until set. Cut into wedges to serve.

Makes 2 servings.

GOOD
Source of
IRON

To make the handle of the skillet ovenproof, wrap it completely in foil.

FOOD CHOICE VALUE	*per serving*
Each Serving: 1/2 of recipe	
3 1/2 ☑ *Protein Choices*	
1 ◪ *Fruits & Vegetables Choice*	
2 ◣ *Fats & Oils Choices*	

12 g	*Carbohydrate*
25 g	*Protein*
22 g	*Total Fat*
1477	*kilojoules (353 Calories)*

Basil-Pepper Sole

Flaky fish layered over crunchy vegetables in a tomato sauce served with piping hot rice, makes for a quick and tasty meal.

1	*medium sweet green pepper, cut in strips*	*1*
125 mL	*sliced onion*	*1/2 cup*
500 g	*sole fillets*	*1 lb*
175 mL	*vegetable or tomato juice*	*3/4 cup*
2 mL	*crushed dried basil*	*1/2 tsp*
500 mL	*hot cooked rice*	*2 cups*

In 3 L (12 x 8 inch) microwaveable baking dish, combine pepper and onion. Cover with vented plastic wrap; microwave at High (100% power) 5 minutes or until just tender, rotating dish once. Drain.

Arrange fish fillets in single layer over vegetables. Combine vegetable juice and basil; pour over fish.

Cover; microwave at High 5 minutes or until fish flakes easily when tested with fork, rotating dish once. Serve with rice.

Makes 4 servings.

Serve with "Budget-Wise Bouillabaisse" soup on page 57.

FOOD CHOICE VALUE *per serving*

Each Serving: 1/4 of recipe

4 ☑ *Protein Choices*
1 ☐ *Starchy Choice*
1 ◪ *Fruits & Vegetables Choice*

27 g	*Carbohydrate*
30 g	*Protein*
8 g	*Total Fat*
1344	*kilojoules (320 Calories)*

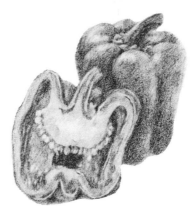

Seafood Stew

Serve in shallow bowls or over pasta, with fresh crusty bread to mop up the savory juices.

1	pkg (284 g/10 oz) frozen cod fillets	1
12	mussels	12
250 mL	sliced celery	1 cup
1	can (284 mL/10 oz) condensed chicken broth plus half soup can water	1
450 mL	spaghetti sauce	1 3/4 cups
250 g	medium shrimp, peeled and deveined	1/2 lb

Separate fish fillets; arrange on microwaveable plate. Microwave, uncovered at High (100% power), 1 minute or until fish is pliable. Cut into 2.5 cm (1 inch) pieces; set aside.

Discard any mussels that do not close when lightly tapped. Scrub mussels under cold running water; remove and discard beards.

In 3 L (12 cup) microwaveable casserole, combine celery and 50 mL (1/4 cup) of the broth. Cover with lid; microwave at High 3 minutes or until celery is tender, stirring once. Stir in remaining broth, water and spaghetti sauce. Cover; microwave at High 5 minutes or until very hot.

Add fish, mussels and shrimp. Cover; microwave at High 8 minutes or until fish flakes easily when tested with fork and mussels open. Discard any unopened mussels.

Makes 4 servings.

MICROWAVEABLE

You can substitute 250 g (1/2 lb) bay scallops or halved sea scallops for the mussels.

EXCELLENT Source of IRON

FOOD CHOICE VALUE	per serving

Each Serving: 1/4 of recipe

4 1/2	☑ *Protein Choices*
2	◩ *Fruits & Vegetables Choices*

22 g	Carbohydrate
33 g	Protein
10 g	Total Fat
1302	kilojoules (310 Calories)

Neptune Chicken

Great for entertaining, the crabmeat and chicken create a melange of textured taste sensations. Serves up scrumptiously in a scallop shell.

MICROWAVEABLE

4	*boneless, skinless chicken breasts (about 500 g/1 lb)*	4
500 mL	*crabmeat*	*2 cups*
15 mL	*vegetable oil*	*1 tbsp*
10 mL	*grated gingerroot*	*2 tsp*
25 mL	*dry sherry*	*2 tbsp*
15 mL	*dried dillweed*	*1 tbsp*
125 mL	*bread crumbs*	*1/2 cup*
25 mL	*butter, melted*	*2 tbsp*

Cut chicken breasts into slivers, about 1 cm (1/4 inch) thick.

Microwave method: In round microwaveable dish, microwave oil at High (100% power) for 1 minute. Add ginger; microwave for 1 minute longer. Add chicken, crab, sherry and dill. Cover and microwave at High for 5 to 6 minutes or until chicken is no longer pink and crab is opaque.

Conventional method: In skillet, sauté ginger in oil for 1 minute. Add chicken, crab, sherry and dill; cover and simmer for 10 minutes or until cooked through.

Both methods: Spoon chicken mixture into 6 scallop shells. Mix bread crumbs with butter; sprinkle over chicken mixture. Broil about 15 cm (6 inches) from heat until crumbs are golden brown. Serve immediately.

Makes 6 servings.

FOOD CHOICE VALUE *per serving*

Each Serving: 1/6 of recipe

4 ☑ *Protein Choices*

1/2 ☐ *Starchy Choice*

8 g	*Carbohydrate*
29 g	*Protein*
10 g	*Total Fat*
1046	*kilojoules (249 Calories)*

MAIN MEALS

EGGS & CHEESE

	Microwave	Protein	Starchy	Fruits & Vegetables	Fats & Oils	Extra	Page
Spanish Omelette		1					187
Leek and Mushroom Flan	●	1 1/2		1	1/2		188
Oriental Omelettes		1 1/2			1	1	189
Vegetarian Strata		2	1	1/2	1/2		190
Manicotti Crepes (Photo: p. 195)		2 1/2	2	1	1 1/2		191
Hearty Cheese & Mushroom Quiche (Photo: p.195)		2 1/2	1		1		192
Spanish Bake (Photo: p. 195)	●	2	1	1/2	1/2		193
Mexican Scramble (Photo: p. 195)	●	1		1/2	1		194
Broccoli Fritatta (Photo: p. 196)	●	3		1/2	1		199
Easy Cheddar Swiss Fondue		1 1/2	1		1 1/2		200
Huevos Rancheros (Photo: p. 197)		1 1/2	1/2	1	2		201

The Food Choice Values on each recipe do not include accompanying foods which are suggested in many of the recipes and shown in some of the photographs.

Spanish Omelette

You can make a light and delicious omelette using only egg whites. It's important to use a nonstick pan over high heat.

2	*egg whites*	*2*
15 mL	*milk*	*1 tbsp*
Pinch	*turmeric or paprika*	*Pinch*
	Salt and pepper	
5 mL	*soft margarine*	*1 tsp*
25 mL	*diced cooked ham (optional)*	*2 tbsp*
25 mL	*finely chopped fresh tomato*	*2 tbsp*
15 mL	*finely chopped green onion*	*1 tbsp*

Whisk egg whites until frothy; add milk, turmeric, and salt and pepper to taste. Heat large nonstick skillet over high heat until hot; add margarine and swirl to cover bottom of pan.

Pour in egg mixture and shake pan over high heat until egg sets. Sprinkle ham (if using), tomato and green onion over egg.

Remove from heat and, using fork, lift one-third of omelette and fold it over centre; tilt pan and roll omelette over onto plate.

Makes 1 serving.

FOOD CHOICE VALUE *per serving*

Each Serving: 1 Omelette

1 ☑ *Protein Choice*

---

3 g	*Carbohydrate*
8 g	*Protein*
4 g	*Total Fat*
333	*kilojoules (79 Calories)*

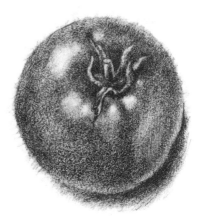

Leek and Mushroom Flan

Serve this fluffy flan for brunch or a quick dinner, with a green vegetable, salad and whole wheat rolls.

250 mL	*thinly sliced leek (white part only)*	*1 cup*
5 mL	*vegetable oil*	*1 tsp*
250 g	*mushrooms, coarsely chopped*	*1/2 lb*
1	*egg, lightly beaten*	*1*
3	*egg whites, lightly beaten*	*3*
25 mL	*milk*	*2 tbsp*
Pinch	*paprika*	*Pinch*
	Salt and pepper	

In 1.5 L (8 1/2 x 4 inch) microwaveable dish, toss leeks with oil. Cover with plastic and microwave at High (100% power) for 1 minute.

Add mushrooms; cover and microwave on High for 4 minutes or until mushrooms are nearly tender. Stir in egg, egg whites, milk, paprika, and salt and pepper to taste.

Microwave, uncovered, on Medium (50% power) for 6 minutes or until mixture is set. Serve hot.

Makes 2 servings.

You can substitute chopped onions for leek.

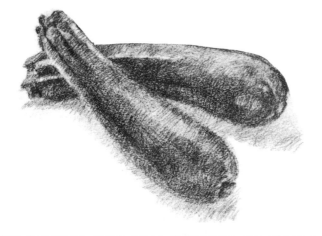

FOOD CHOICE VALUE *per serving*

Each Serving: 1/2 of recipe

1 1/2	⬲	*Protein Choices*
1	◨	*Fruits & Vegetables Choice*
1/2	◣	*Fats & Oils Choice*

15 g	*Carbohydrate*
12 g	*Protein*
6 g	*Total Fat*
642	*kilojoules* (153 Calories)

Oriental Omelettes

This is as easy to make as a Western Omelette, but it has all the flavors of the Far East.

4	eggs, lightly beaten	4
1 mL	salt	1/4 tsp
1 mL	ginger	1/4 tsp
500 mL	chopped fresh bean sprouts	2 cups
1	can (213 g/7.5 oz) salmon, drained and flaked	1
2	green onions, finely chopped	2
1	stalk celery, chopped	1
15 mL	chopped fresh parsley	1 tbsp
	Vegetable oil	

In bowl, combine eggs, salt, ginger, bean sprouts, salmon, onions, celery and parsley.

Heat small amount of oil in large skillet (preferably nonstick). Drop 25 mL (2 tbsp) mixture into pan. Cook over medium heat, turning once, until lightly browned. Remove from pan; keep warm. Repeat with remaining mixture.

Makes about 24 patties or 6 servings.

FOOD CHOICE VALUE *per serving*

Each Serving: 4 Patties (1/6 recipe)

1 1/2 ◨ *Protein Choices*

1 ▲ *Fats & Oils Choice*

1 ✚ *Extra*

3 g	Carbohydrate
10 g	Protein
9 g	Total Fat
567	kilojoules *(135 Calories)*

Vegetarian Strata

For the easiest of elegant entertaining, combine the ingredients
in advance, then bake when guests arrive.

375 mL	*sliced fresh mushrooms*	*1 1/2 cups*
1	*medium tomato, diced*	*1*
125 mL	*diced sweet green pepper*	*1/2 cup*
125 mL	*finely chopped onion*	*1/2 cup*
1.25 mL	*cubed bread (5 to 6 slices)*	*5 cups*
250 mL	*shredded part-skim Cheddar cheese*	*1 cup*
4	*eggs*	*4*
500 mL	*milk*	*2 cups*
1 mL	*salt*	*1/4 tsp*
2 mL	*paprika*	*1/2 tsp*
1 mL	*each dried oregano and basil*	*1/4 tsp*

In bowl, combine mushrooms, tomato, green pepper and onion.

In greased 2 L (8 cup) casserole, layer half the bread cubes, half the
vegetable mixture and half the cheese. Repeat layers.

Whisk together eggs, milk, salt, paprika, oregano and basil.
Pour over strata. Cover and chill at least 3 hours or overnight.

Bake in 180°C (350°F) oven, uncovered, for 1 to 1 1/4 hours or until
knife inserted in centre comes out clean. Serve immediately.

Makes 6 servings.

*Paprika is mild , slightly sweet
and bright red in color. Use this
color as a garnish to brighten any
light colored food. Sprinkle on fish,
potatoes, eggs, poultry, cream
sauces.*

FOOD CHOICE VALUE *per serving*

Each Serving: 1/6 of recipe

- 2 ☑ *Protein Choices*
- 1 ☐ *Starchy Choice*
- 1/2 ◪ *Fruits & Vegetables Choice*
- 1/2 ◤ *Fats & Oils Choice*

21 g	*Carbohydrate*
15 g	*Protein*
9 g	*Total Fat*
965	*kilojoules (231 Calories)*

Manicotti Crepes

Perfect for entertaining, this meatless dish is healthy, too. Serve with a tossed salad of crisp, fresh greens.

4	*eggs*	*4*
1 mL	*salt*	*1/4 tsp*
500 mL	*all-purpose flour*	*2 cups*
500 mL	*milk*	*2 cups*
50 mL	*melted margarine or vegetable oil*	*1/4 cup*
	FILLING	
750 mL	*pressed low-fat cottage cheese*	*3 cups*
2	*eggs, beaten*	*2*
5 mL	*salt*	*1 tsp*
2 mL	*pepper*	*1/2 tsp*
25 mL	*dried parsley flakes*	*2 tbsp*
50 mL	*Parmesan cheese grated*	*1/4 cup*
750 mL	*spaghetti sauce (tomato)*	*3 cups*
500 mL	*shredded low-fat mozzarella cheese*	*2 cups*

In bowl, beat eggs and salt. Alternately add flour and milk, beating until smooth. Add butter and beat until uniform. Let stand at room temperature for 1 hour.

Heat 25 cm (10 inch) nonstick crepe pan on medium-high heat until hot enough to sizzle a drop of water. Grease lightly. Using 75 mL (1/3 cup) batter for each crepe, rotate pan to coat bottom, cook crepe until lightly brown on both sides.

Filling: Combine cottage cheese, eggs, salt, pepper, parsley and Parmesan; place 25 mL (2 tbsp) in each crepe and roll up. Place crepes in large shallow baking dish. Spread spaghetti sauce over crepes and top with mozzarella. Bake in 190°C (375°F) oven for 30 minutes or until bubbly and filling is set.

Makes 10 servings.

PHOTO ON PAGE 195.

When it comes to building and maintaining strong bones, calcium is tops. It's especially important for growing children and those who are prone to calcium deficiencies as they get older.

FOOD CHOICE VALUE *per serving*

Each Serving: 1/10 of recipe

2 1/2 ☑ *Protein Choices*
2 ☐ *Starchy Choices*
1 ◪ *Fruits & Vegetables Choice*
1 1/2 ◣ *Fats & Oils Choices*

38 g *Carbohydrate*
22 g *Protein*
16 g *Total Fat*
1621 *kilojoules* (387 Calories)

Hearty Cheese & Mushroom Quiche

This interesting variation of quiche has a surprise crust of hash brown potatoes. Serve with a fresh vegetable or salad for a complete meal.

PHOTO ON PAGE 195.

25 mL	*butter or soft margarine*	*2 tbsp*
500 mL	*frozen hash brown potatoes*	*2 cups*
2 mL	*celery salt*	*1/2 tsp*
175 mL	*sliced fresh mushrooms*	*3/4 cup*
125 mL	*chopped onion*	*1/2 cup*
125 mL	*chopped sweet green pepper*	*1/2 cup*
5	*eggs*	*5*
125 mL	*milk*	*1/2 cup*
Pinch	*pepper*	*Pinch*
250 mL	*shredded Cheddar cheese (low 15% fat)*	*1 cup*
6	*slices back bacon, cooked and crumbled*	*6*

In skillet, melt butter over medium-high heat. Sauté potatoes until browned and crusty, about 5 minutes. Sprinkle with celery salt and mix well. Spread evenly in 23 cm (9 inch) pie plate or quiche dish. Top with mushrooms, onion and green pepper.

Whisk together eggs, milk and pepper. Pour into pan. Bake in 160°C (325°F) oven for 30 minutes or until set. Remove from oven; sprinkle with cheese and bacon.

Makes 6 servings.

FOOD CHOICE VALUE *per serving*

Each Serving: 1/6 of recipe

2 1/2 ☑ *Protein Choices*

1 ☐ *Starchy Choice*

1 ▲ *Fats & Oils Choice*

---

17 g   *Carbohydrate*

19 g   *Protein*

12 g   *Total Fat*

1074   *kilojoules (257 Calories)*

Spanish Bake

PHOTO ON PAGE 195.

Delicious for either a light dinner, lunch or weekend brunch, here's a neat Spanish twist to really warm up the family on a cold winter day. Control the "warmth" by the amount of chili powder.

6 slices	*back bacon, chopped*	*6*
125 mL	*coarsely chopped celery*	*1/2 cup*
125 mL	*coarsely chopped onion*	*1/2 cup*
1	*can (540 mL/19 oz) tomatoes, drained and chopped*	*1*
5 mL	*chili powder*	*1 tsp*
1 mL	*salt*	*1/4 tsp*
4	*eggs*	*4*
4	*slices toast*	*4*

In 1 L (4 cup) microwaveable measure, microwave bacon on High (100% power) 5 to 6 minutes or until crisp, stirring several times. Drain bacon and set aside; reserve 15 mL (1 tbsp) drippings.

Add celery and onion to drippings. Microwave on High 2 minutes or until cooked. Add tomatoes, reserved bacon, chili powder and salt. Cover with vented plastic wrap. Microwave on High 4 minutes or until boiling.

Divide tomato mixture among four individual shallow 250 mL (1 cup) baking dishes. Break one egg into each dish; pierce yolk membrane with fork. Microwave on Medium-High (70% power) 8 to 10 minutes or until eggs are cooked as desired. Serve with toast.

Makes 4 servings.

FOOD CHOICE VALUE *per serving*

Each Serving: 1/4 of recipe

2	✓ *Protein Choices*
1	☐ *Starchy Choice*
1/2	◨ *Fruits & Vegetables Choice*
1/2	▲ *Fats & Oils Choice*

21 g	*Carbohydrate*
18 g	*Protein*
9 g	*Total Fat*
1013	*kilojoules* (243 Calories)

Mexican Scramble

Dress up scrambled eggs with colorful chunks of vegetables
and zippy flavor. This recipe is flexible to a variety of meal times.
Kids love them for lunch - served in tacos.

PHOTO ON PAGE 195.

5 mL	*butter or soft margarine*	*1 tsp*
1	*small tomato, seeded and chopped*	*1*
50 mL	*chopped sweet green pepper*	*1/4 cup*
50 mL	*chopped green onions*	*1/4 cup*
15 mL	*canned chopped green chilies, drained*	*1 tbsp*
Pinch	*ground cumin*	*Pinch*
6	*eggs*	*6*
25 mL	*low-fat yogurt*	*2 tbsp*
1 mL	*salt*	*1/4 tsp*

*For a special treat, serve topped with
low-fat shredded cheese in crisp taco
shells lined with leaf lettuce.*

Melt butter in 500 mL (2 cup) microwaveable measure. Stir in
tomato, green pepper, green onions, chilies and cumin. Microwave
on High (100% power) 2 minutes or until vegetables are cooked.

In 1 L (4 cup) microwaveable measure, beat together eggs, yogurt
and salt. Microwave on Medium-High (70% power) 3 minutes.

Stir in cooked vegetables. Microwave on Medium-High 2 minutes
longer or until eggs are set. Stir. Cover and let stand 2 to 3 minutes
before serving.

Makes 4 servings.

FOOD CHOICE VALUE *per serving*

Each Serving: 1/4 of recipe

1   ☑ *Protein Choice*

1/2   ◪ *Fruits & Vegetables Choice*

1   ▲ *Fats & Oils Choice*

3 g	*Carbohydrate*
10 g	*Protein*
9 g	*Total Fat*
567	*kilojoules (135 Calories)*

Manicotti Crepes (p.191)

Spanish Bake (p.193) and Mexican Scramble (p.194)

Hearty Cheese and Mushroom Quiche (p.192)

Broccoli Fritatta (p.199)

Pastaccio: Greek Lasagna (p.203)

Fettuccini with Grilled Turkey (p.212)

Overnight Lean Lasagna (p.214)

Huevos Rancheros (p.201)

Vegetable Lasagna Swirls (p.205)

Penne with Beef Strips (p.206)

Pepper Steak Pasta Salad (p.204)

Broccoli Frittata

PHOTO ON PAGE 196.

Microwave Cooking Tip:
To ensure even cooking of dishes
like frittata and quiche, set the
dish on an inverted saucer or on
an elevating accessory.

FOOD CHOICE VALUE *per serving*

Each Serving: 1/4 of recipe

3 ☑ *Protein Choices*
1/2 ▢ *Fruits & Vegetables Choice*
1 ▲ *Fats & Oils Choice*

7 g   *Carbohydrate*
21 g   *Protein*
15 g   *Total Fat*
1061   *kilojoules* (254 Calories)

Spruce up your leftover vegetables with this delightful dish that's packed with Calcium and Iron. Be careful not to overcook the broccoli. Serve with green beans and whole wheat rolls.

250 mL	*frozen chopped broccoli*	*1 cup*
125 mL	*chopped ham*	*1/2 cup*
5 mL	*vegetable oil*	*1 tsp*
1	*small onion, quartered and sliced*	*1*
250 mL	*shredded part-skim Swiss cheese*	*1 cup*
1 mL	*salt*	*1/4 tsp*
6	*eggs*	*6*
50 mL	*milk*	*3 tbsp*
1 mL	*garlic powder*	*1/4 tsp*
	ground nutmeg (optional)	

In 500 mL (2 cup) microwaveable measure, microwave broccoli on High (100% power) 2 minutes or until tender-crisp. Drain. Spread on bottom of greased 23 cm (9 inch) microwaveable pie plate. Sprinkle ham over broccoli.

In 500 mL (2 cup) microwaveable measure, combine oil and onion. Microwave on High 1 minute. Stir; microwave on High 1 minute longer. Spread over ham layer. Sprinkle cheese and salt over all.

Beat together eggs, milk and garlic powder. Pour over cheese. Sprinkle with nutmeg (if using). Cover loosely with waxed paper. Place on 2.5 cm (1 inch) high microwaveable rack. Microwave on Medium-High (70% power) 7 minutes or until set.

Makes 4 servings.

Easy Cheddar Swiss Fondue

This simple and satifying recipe will have you scurrying to your closet to get out that fondue pot you haven't used in so long. Serve with extra fresh veggies for dipping. A great way to have some fun and conversation with good friends.

500 mL	*shredded Cheddar cheese*	*2 cups*
500 mL	*shredded Swiss cheese*	*2 cups*
50 mL	*all-purpose flour*	*1/4 cup*
300 mL	*dry white wine or beer**	*1 1/4 cups*
4 mL	*salt*	*3/4 tsp*
Pinch	*garlic powder*	*Pinch*
	French bread cubes	

Combine Cheddar and Swiss cheeses. Sprinkle with flour; toss lightly to coat.

In saucepan, heat wine until simmering but not boiling. Gradually add cheese mixture, by small handfuls, stirring constantly after each addition until cheese melts (mixture will appear curdled at first). Stir in salt and garlic powder.

Transfer to fondue pot and keep warm. Serve with bread cubes for dipping.

Makes 11 servings, about 675 mL (2 3/4 cups).

*Ask your dietitian or doctor about the use alcohol.

FOOD CHOICE VALUE	*per serving*
Each Serving: 84 g (3 oz) with	
20 g Bread Cubes	
1 1/2 ☑ *Protein Choices*	
1 ☐ *Starchy Choice*	
1 1/2 ▲ *Fats & Oils Choices*	

15 g	*Carbohydrate*
13 g	*Protein*
13 g	*Total Fat*
962	*kilojoules (229 Calories)*

Huevos Rancheros

PHOTO ON PAGE 197.

This zesty Mexican egg bake is often served for brunch. When accompanied by refried beans and tortillas, it's a great supper dish too.

Mexican spice tomatoes contribute a great extra seasoning flavor. The tomato sauce mixture may be prepared ahead of time and reheated before baking.

*Recipe has been developed for use with 19 oz or 28 oz can sizes. Nutritional analysis based on 19 oz size only.

15 mL	vegetable oil	1 tbsp
1	medium onion, chopped	1
1	medium sweet green pepper, chopped	1
15 mL	all-purpose flour	1 tbsp
1	can (540 mL/19 oz)* Mexican spice stewed tomatoes	1
1	can (341 mL/12 oz) corn, drained	1
10 mL	Worcestershire sauce	2 tsp
6	eggs	6
250 mL	shredded Cheddar cheese	1 cup

In saucepan, heat oil over medium heat; cook onion and green pepper about 3 minutes or until tender. Stir in flour; add tomatoes, corn and Worcestershire sauce; bring to boil.

Pour into 3.5 L (13 x 9 inch) baking dish. Break eggs into tomato mixture. Bake in 180°C (350°F) oven for 15 minutes. Sprinkle with cheese; bake until eggs are cooked, 3 to 5 minutes longer.

Makes 6 servings, each 250 g/9 oz.

FOOD CHOICE VALUE *per serving*

Each Serving: 1/6 recipe

1 1/2 ☑ *Protein Choices*

1/2 ☐ *Starchy Choice*

1 ◪ *Fruits & Vegetables Choice*

2 ◣ *Fats & Oils Choices*

17 g   *Carbohydrate*

13 g   *Protein*

14 g   *Total Fat*

1042   *kilojoules (248 Calories)*

MAIN MEALS

PASTA

	Protein	Starchy	Fruits & Vegetables	Fats & Oils	Page
Pastaccio: Greek Lasagna *(Photo: p. 196)*	3 1/2	1	1/2	1	203
Pepper Steak Pasta Salad *(Photo: p. 198)*	3 1/2	1	1		204
Vegetable Lasagna Swirls *(Photo: p. 198)*	1	1/2	1	1	205
Penne with Beef Strips *(Photo: p. 198)*	2	1	1/2		206
Italian Pork 'n Pepper Pasta	3	1	1 1/2	2	207
Second Act Pasta	3	2			208
Pasta & Turkey Skillet Supper	3	2	1		209
Pasta "Du Jour"	3	2	1		210
Company Pasta	2 1/2	2	1/2		211
Fettuccini with Grilled Turkey *(Photo: p. 197)*	3 1/2	1 1/2	1/2		212
Garden Pork Pasta	2	1 1/2	1		213
Overnight Lean Lasagna *(Photo: p. 197)*	4	1	1		214

The Food Choice Values on each recipe do not include accompanying foods which are suggested in many of the recipes and shown in some of the photographs.

Pasticcio: Greek Lasagna

PHOTO ON PAGE 196.

Italy meets Greece in this wonderful recipe that combines the best of both worlds in a savory feast that will feed a crowd or keep the family going to the fridge for leftovers.

750 mL	cooked macaroni	3 cups
2	eggs, lightly beaten	2
75 mL	grated Parmesan cheese	1/3 cup
	FILLING	
750 g	lean ground beef	1 1/2 lb
500 mL	sliced mushrooms	2 cups
1 cup	chopped onion	250 mL
1	can (398 mL/14 oz) tomato sauce	1
5 mL	each garlic powder, dried oregano and basil	1 tsp
1 mL	each salt and pepper	1/4 tsp
0.5 mL	cinnamon	1/8 tsp
	TOPPING	
25 mL	butter or soft margarine	2 tbsp
75 mL	all-purpose flour	1/3 cup
1 mL	each salt and nutmeg	1/4 tsp
750 mL	milk	3 cups
2	eggs, lightly beaten	2
75 mL	grated Parmesan cheese	1/3 cup

Combine macaroni, eggs and cheese. Spread in greased 3.5 L (13 x 9 inch) baking dish. Set aside.

Filling: In large skillet, cook beef, mushrooms and onion until tender and browned. Drain off fat. Stir in tomato sauce, garlic, oregano, basil, salt, pepper and cinnamon; simmer, uncovered, while preparing topping.

Topping: In large saucepan, melt butter; stir in flour, salt and nutmeg. Add milk; cook, stirring, until thickened and bubbly. Gradually stir some of the mixture into eggs, then return to saucepan. Cook over low heat 1 minute longer.

Spread filling over macaroni; pour sauce over top. Sprinkle with Parmesan. Bake in 180°C (350°F) oven for 35 to 40 minutes or until golden brown and bubbly.

Makes 10 servings.

FOOD CHOICE VALUE *per serving*

Each Serving: 1/10 of recipe

3 1/2 ☑ *Protein Choices*

1 ☐ *Starchy Choice*

1/2 ◩ *Fruits & Vegetables Choice*

1 ▲ *Fats & Oils Choice*

---

22 g   Carbohydrate

26 g   Protein

16 g   Total Fat

1371   kilojoules *(328 Calories)*

Pepper Steak Pasta Salad

Brimming with flavor, color and texture, this make-ahead salad is
a delicious main meal plus is great to have on hand in the refrigerator
for a fast meal, picnics or ski lunches.

PHOTO ON PAGE 198.

15 mL	*olive oil*	*1 tbsp*
15 mL	*red wine vinegar*	*1 tbsp*
15 mL	*beef stock*	*1 tbsp*
1–2	*cloves garlic, minced*	*1–2*
750 g	*Round or Sirloin Tip Steak*	*1 1/2 lb*
500 mL	*rotini noodles*	*2 cups*
Half	*each, sweet red and green pepper, julienned*	*Half*
125 mL	*small cauliflower florets*	*1/2 cup*
125 mL	*small broccoli florets*	*1/2 cup*
2	*carrots, julienned*	*2*
2	*green onions, thinly sliced*	*2*
250 mL	*light Italian or Caesar-style salad dressing*	*1 cup*
2 mL	*salt*	*1/2 tsp*
	grated Parmesan cheese (optional)	

*To julienne, or cut vegetables
into matchstick-size pieces, slice
them lengthwise into about 3 mm
(1/8 inch) thickness. Then, with
cut side down, cut lengthwise into
strips. Cut crosswise into 5 cm
(2 inch) pieces.*

In shallow baking dish, combine oil, vinegar, beef stock, garlic,
and pepper to taste. Pierce steak at regular intervals with fork; add
to marinade and turn to coat. Cover and refrigerate to marinate for
8 hours or overnight, turning occasionally.

Remove steaks from marinade. Broil for 4 to 5 minutes per side
for medium-rare. Cut in very thin slices diagonally across the grain.

Meanwhile, cook pasta in boiling water, until tender but still
firm; drain and rinse in cold water. Blanch cauliflower, broccoli
and carrots; cool immediately in ice water and pat dry.

In large bowl, combine steak, pasta, cauliflower, broccoli, carrots,
red and green peppers, onions, salad dressing, salt, and pepper to
taste. Let stand for 1 hour to blend flavours. Garnish with Parmesan
cheese, if desired.

Makes 6 servings.

FOOD CHOICE VALUE *per serving*

Each Serving : 1/6 of recipe

3 1/2	☑ *Protein Choices*
1	☐ *Starchy Choice*
1	◪ *Fruits & Vegetables Choice*

27 g	*Carbohydrate*
27 g	*Protein*
9 g	*Total Fat*
1247	*kilojoules (297 Calories)*

Vegetable Lasagna Swirls

This creative way to serve lasagna is a showstopper. Elegant for presentation to guests yet fun-to-eat for kids

PHOTO ON PAGE 198.

If desired, you can bake this in the traditional way. Alternately layer half the lasagna noodles, half the vegetable-cheese mixture and half the sauce in a shallow 3 L (12 cup) rectangular baking dish. Repeat layers and bake as directed.

50 mL	butter	3 tbsp
1 L	chopped fresh mushrooms	4 cups
250 mL	chopped onion	1 cup
1	pkg (300 g) chopped frozen spinach, thawed and squeezed dry	1
2	eggs, beaten	2
500 mL	shredded mozzarella cheese	2 cups
250 mL	cottage cheese	1 cup
125 mL	grated Parmesan cheese	1/2 cup
	Salt and pepper	
8	lasagna noodles, cooked and drained	8
3	cans (213 mL/7.5 oz each) pizza sauce	3

In large frypan, melt butter; sauté mushrooms and onion until tender and any liquid has evaporated; cool. Stir in spinach, eggs, mozzarella, cottage and Parmesan cheeses. Add salt and pepper to taste.

Spread about 175 mL (3/4 cup) cheese mixture along each noodle to within 2.5 cm (1 inch) of one end. Roll up from filled end. Carefully cut rolls in half crosswise.

Spread pizza sauce in shallow 2 L (8 cup) baking dish. Arrange rolls, curly end up, in sauce. Cover and bake in 180°C (350°F) oven 45 to 50 minutes.

Makes 16 servings.

FOOD CHOICE VALUE *per serving*

Each Serving: 1/16 of recipe

1 1/2 ☑ *Protein Choices*

1/2 ☐ *Starchy Choice*

1 ◪ *Fruits & Vegetables Choice*

1 1/2 ◣ *Fats & Oils Choices*

---

18 g *Carbohydrate*

11 g *Protein*

11 g *Total Fat*

899 *kilojoules (214 Calories)*

Penne with Beef Strips

Here's the freshness of a stir-fry combined with the comfort of pasta.

15 mL	*vegetable oil*	*1 tbsp*
500 g	*top round steak, cut in thin strips*	*1 lb*
2	*cloves garlic, minced*	*2*
25 mL	*finely chopped onion*	*2 tbsp*
5 mL	*each dried basil, thyme and oregano*	*1 tsp*
1	*can (540 mL/19 oz) tomatoes, puréed*	*1*
1	*sweet green pepper, thinly sliced*	*1*
750 mL	*penne or rigatoni pasta*	*3 cups*
	Pepper	
	Freshly grated Parmesan cheese	

In heavy skillet, heat oil over medium-high heat; stir-fry beef for 1 minute. Add garlic, onion, basil, thyme and oregano; cook 2 minutes or until beef is no longer pink. Push to side of pan.

Stir tomatoes into pan juices, then mix with beef. Reduce heat and simmer 15 minutes or until beef is tender. Add green peppers during last 2 minutes of cooking.

Meanwhile, in large pot, cook pasta in boiling water until tender but firm. Drain and add to beef mixture; toss to mix. Season with pepper and sprinkle with Parmesan to taste.

Makes 8 servings, each 180 g/6 1/2 oz.

PHOTO ON PAGE 198.

FOOD CHOICE VALUE *per serving*

Each Serving: 1/8 of recipe

2	☑	*Protein Choices*
1	☐	*Starchy Choice*
1/2	◩	*Fruits & Vegetables Choice*

24 g	*Carbohydrate*
17 g	*Protein*
4 g	*Total Fat*
825	*kilojoules (197 Calories)*

Italian Pork 'n Pepper Pasta

Quick and easy to prepare pasta(any variety), is turned into a taste sensation with this recipe that will have you singing "that's amoré" with every bite you take.

Also makes for great Mini Meal leftovers and packed lunches.

375 g	*pork loin or leg,*	*3/4 lb*
	cut in 5 x 1 cm (2 x 1/2-inch) strips	
45 mL	*vegetable oil*	*3 tbsp*
25 mL	*red wine vinegar*	*2 tbsp*
10 mL	*Italian seasoning*	*2 tsp*
2	*cloves garlic, crushed*	*2*
1	*medium onion, finely chopped*	*1*
1	*sweet pepper (red, green or yellow), cut in strips*	*1*
500 mL	*sliced fresh mushrooms*	*2 cups*
125 mL	*beef broth*	*1/2 cup*
125 mL	*spaghetti sauce*	*1/2 cup*
500 mL	*cooked pasta*	*2 cups*
15 mL	*grated Parmesan cheese*	*1 tbsp*

In small bowl, combine pork strips with 25 mL (2 tbsp) of oil, vinegar, Italian seasoning and garlic. Marinate for 20 minutes.

Heat heavy skillet over high heat; add pork mixture and cook, stirring, 3 minutes. Remove pork from pan, set aside and keep warm.

Add remaining oil to pan. Sauté onion over medium heat until tender. Add pepper and mushrooms; sauté 5 minutes. Stir in beef broth and simmer 3 minutes. Add spaghetti sauce. Return pork to pan; cook 1 to 2 minutes longer or until heated through. Toss with pasta and sprinkle with Parmesan cheese.

Makes 4 servings.

FOOD CHOICE VALUE *per serving*

Each Serving: 1/4 of recipe

3	◪ *Protein Choices*
1	◻ *Starchy Choice*
1 1/2	◪ *Fruits & Vegetables Choices*
2	◣ *Fats & Oils Choice*

30 g	*Carbohydrate*
23 g	*Protein*
20 g	*Total Fat*
1646	*kilojoules (392 Calories)*

Second Act Pasta

No one will guess this hearty stir-fry came from yesterday's leftovers. It's quick and easy and tastes great. Any vegetable can be used – leftover or fresh!

500 mL	*chicken broth*	*2 cups*
1	*sweet green pepper, sliced*	*1*
3	*carrots, thinly sliced*	*3*
1	*small onion, finely chopped*	*1*
25 mL	*all-purpose flour*	*2 tbsp*
375 to 500 mL	*cooked pork, cut into thin strips*	*1 1/2 to 2 cups*
7 mL	*Worcestershire sauce*	*1 1/2 tsp*
125 mL	*shredded skim milk mozzarella cheese*	*1/2 cup*
	Salt and pepper	
500 mL	*cooked penne or macaroni*	*2 cups*

In large nonstick pan, heat 125 mL (1/2 cup) broth over medium heat. Add pepper, carrots and onion; cover and cook, stirring occasionally, until vegetables are soft, about 5 minutes.

Sprinkle flour over vegetables and mix well; slowly add remaining broth, stirring constantly. Add pork and Worcestershire sauce, mixing well; cook for 3 minutes. Add cheese; season with salt and pepper to taste. Cook for 1 minute, stirring constantly. Add penne and serve immediately.

Makes 4 servings.

FOOD CHOICE VALUE *per serving*

Each Serving: 1/4 of recipe

3	☑	*Protein Choices*
2	☐	*Starchy Choices*

31 g	*Carbohydrate*
25 g	*Protein*
10 g	*Total Fat*
1340	*kilojoules* (319 Calories)

Pasta and Turkey Skillet Supper

This dish combines two favorite and nutritious ingredients, embellished with the savoury additions of basil, oregano and thyme. Combined in a rich tomato sauce laced with garlic and mushrooms, skillet pasta has never been better.

Ground turkey is a low-fat blend of primarily all-dark meat. Because of its delicate mild flavor, ground turkey requires more seasoning than other ground meats.

500 mL	rotini pasta	2 cups
500 g	ground turkey	1 lb
500 mL	sliced mushrooms	2 cups
2	cloves garlic, minced	2
250 mL	finely chopped fresh spinach	1 cup
2 mL	each dried basil, oregano and thyme	1/2 tsp
1	can (398 mL/14 oz) tomato sauce	1
125 mL	grated Parmesan cheese	1/2 cup

Cook pasta according to package directions.

Meanwhile, in large nonstick skillet, combine turkey, mushrooms and garlic. Cook over medium-high heat, stirring and separating turkey as it cooks, 5 minutes or until moisture evaporates.

Add spinach, basil, oregano, thyme and tomato sauce; cook 5 minutes or until thickened.

Drain pasta. Spoon meat sauce over pasta and sprinkle with Parmesan cheese. Serve immediately.

Makes 6 servings, each 300 g/11 oz.

FOOD CHOICE VALUE *per serving*

Each Serving: 1/6 of recipe

3 ☑ *Protein Choices*

2 ☐ *Starchy Choices*

1 ◪ *Fruits & Vegetables Choice*

---

44 g   *Carbohydrate*

27 g   *Protein*

 9 g   *Total Fat*

1533 *kilojoules (366 Calories)*

Pasta "Du Jour"

Or maybe the "jour" after, since this recipe makes terrific use
of leftover vegetables and chicken.

500 mL	*pasta*	*2 cups*
50 mL	*all-purpose flour*	*1/4 cup*
500 mL	*chicken broth*	*2 cups*
15 mL	*fresh dill*	*1 tbsp*
1 mL	*pepper*	*1 tsp*
500 mL	*cooked chopped chicken*	*2 cups*
750 mL	*cooked frozen mixed vegetables*	*3 cups*
125 mL	*small salad shrimp, cooked (optional)*	*1/2 cup*
Half	*sweet red pepper, chopped*	*Half*

Cook pasta according to manufacturer's instructions.

In large saucepan, blend flour into broth. Add dill and pepper;
cook over medium heat, stirring frequently until thickened.

Add chicken, vegetables, shrimp (if using), red pepper and pasta;
cook until heated through.

Makes 6 servings.

*A great recipe for adding variety to
meal planning. Let family members
take turns on picking their favorite
pasta for this tasty meal.*

GOOD
Source of
IRON

FOOD CHOICE VALUE *per serving*

Each Serving: 1/6 of recipe

3	☑	*Protein Choices*
2	☐	*Starchy Choices*
1	◨	*Fruits & Vegetables Choice*

38 g	*Carbohydrate*
25 g	*Protein*
5 g	*Total Fat*
1235	*kilojoules (294 Calories)*

Company Pasta

A great dish for when company's expected, this recipe turns any plain pasta into a crowd pleaser with the addition of chicken, ham, pine nuts and artichokes.

This recipe is great for feeding a crowd of guests, but portions are small. Plan to serve with extra side dish recipes or vegetables.

The marinade drained from the artichoke hearts can be used elsewhere as a tasty salad dressing.

500 g	*dried pasta (such as rotini)*	*1 lb*
50 mL	*all-purpose flour*	*1/4 cup*
1 L	*chicken broth*	*4 cups*
750 mL	*diced cooked chicken*	*3 cups*
250 mL	*diced cooked ham*	*1 cup*
75 mL	*pine nuts*	*1/3 cup*
1	*jar (170 mL/6 oz)*	*1*
	marinated artichoke hearts, drained	
Half	*sweet green pepper, diced*	*Half*
Half	*sweet red pepper, diced*	*Half*
10 mL	*dried basil*	*2 tsp*
5 mL	*oregano*	*1 tsp*
50 mL	*grated Parmesan cheese*	*1/4 cup*

Prepare pasta according to package instructions; drain well.

Meanwhile, in a large pot, blend flour into chicken broth; cook over medium heat, stirring frequently, until thickened.

Stir in pasta, chicken, ham, pine nuts, artichoke hearts, green and red pepper, basil and oregano, stirring well to combine. Cover and simmer until heated through. Serve sprinkled with Parmesan cheese.

Makes 12 small servings.

FOOD CHOICE VALUE *per serving*

Each Serving: 1/12 of recipe

2 1/2 ☑ *Protein Choices*

2 ☐ *Starchy Choices*

1/2 ◨ *Fruits & Vegetables Choice*

---

36 g   *Carbohydrate*

23 g   *Protein*

9 g   *Total Fat*

1316   *kilojoules (313 Calories)*

Fettuccini with Grilled Turkey

A colorful combination of vegetables and fettuccini make an
attractive accompaniment for tasty herbed turkey cutlets.

4	*turkey cutlets (100 g /3 oz each)*	*4*
	Juice of 1 lemon	
2 mL	*each crushed dried basil, thyme and oregano*	*1/2 tsp*
100 g	*spinach fettuccini*	*3 oz*
2	*medium zucchini, julienned*	*2*
2	*medium carrots, julienned*	*2*
15 mL	*vegetable oil*	*1 tbsp*
	Pepper	

Pound turkey cutlets to 5 mm (1/4 inch) thickness. Brush cutlets
with lemon juice. Combine basil, thyme and oregano; sprinkle over
both sides of cutlets. Grill turkey until no longer pink inside.

Meanwhile, cook fettuccini, drain and keep warm.

Blanch zucchini and carrots; drain. In skillet, heat oil; stir-fry
zucchini and carrots lightly. Add pepper to taste; stir in drained
fettuccini. Serve with turkey cutlets.

Makes 4 servings, each 350 g/12.5 oz.

PHOTO ON PAGE 197.

*Serve turkey with light, but flavorful
vegetable- and fruit-based sauces
instead of gravy. Fresh herbs, such
as basil, thyme, oregano and ginger,
complement turkey's delicate flavor
and eliminate the need for salt
during cooking or at the table.*

GOOD
Source of
IRON

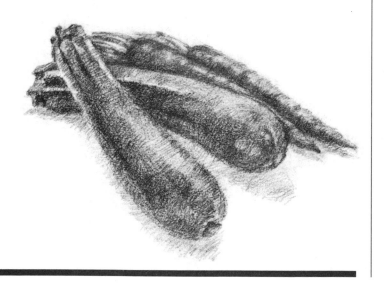

FOOD CHOICE VALUE	*per serving*
Each Serving: 1/4 recipe	
3 1/2 ☑ *Protein Choices*	
1 1/2 ☐ *Starchy Choices*	
1/2 ◪ *Fruits & Vegetables Choice*	

30 g	*Carbohydrate*
28 g	*Protein*
5 g	*Total Fat*
1147	*kilojoules (273 Calories)*

Garden Pork Pasta

If you prefer, you can substitute broccoli florets for the zucchini.

375 g	*fettucine*	*3/4 lb*
15 mL	*vegetable oil*	*1 tbsp*
2	*cloves garlic, minced*	*2*
500 g	*pork tenderloin or pork butt,*	*1 lb*
	cut into 5 x 1 cm x 3 mm (2 x 1/2 x 1/8 inch) strips	
4	*green onion stalks, chopped*	*4*
1	*zucchini, cut into 2.5 cm x 3 mm (1 x 1/8 inch) strips*	*1*
125 g	*snow peas*	*1/4 lb*
500 mL	*sliced mushrooms*	*2 cups*
half	*sweet red pepper, cut into strips*	*half*
5 mL	*dried basil*	*1 tsp*
2 mL	*dried oregano*	*1/2 tsp*
125 mL	*chicken stock*	*1/2 cup*
15 mL	*cornstarch*	*1 tbsp*
25 mL	*cold water*	*2 tbsp*
2 mL	*salt*	*1/2 tsp*
1 mL	*pepper*	*1/4 tsp*
50 mL	*grated Romano or Parmesan cheese*	*1/4 cup*

Cook fettucine as per package instructions; drain.

Meanwhile, in large deep skillet or wok, heat oil over medium-high heat; sauté garlic and pork until lightly browned. Add onions, zucchini, snow peas, mushrooms, red pepper, basil, oregano and chicken stock; simmer for about 7 minutes or until vegetables are tender-crisp.

Combine cornstarch and water; stir into pan and bring to boil. Season with salt and pepper. Toss with fettucine and cheese. Serve immediately.

Makes 4 servings.

FOOD CHOICE VALUE *per serving*

Each Serving: 1/8 of recipe

2 ☑ *Protein Choices*

1 1/2 ☐ *Starchy Choices*

1 ☑ *Fruits & Vegetables Choice*

---

34 g   *Carbohydrate*

19 g   *Protein*

5 g   *Total Fat*

1079   *kilojoules (257 Calories)*

Overnight Lean Lasagna

This traditional lasagna recipe has been adapted to today's taste and lifestyle.

PHOTO ON PAGE 197.

500 g	lean ground beef or ground chicken	1 lb
1	can (540 mL/19 oz)* tomatoes	1
5 mL	dried basil	1 tsp
2 mL	dried thyme	1/2 tsp
500 mL	low-fat cottage cheese	2 cups
2	green onions, cut in pieces	2
2 mL	dried oregano	1/2 tsp
9	lasagna noodles	9
500 mL	shredded part-skim mozzarella cheese	2 cups
50 mL	grated Parmesan cheese	1/4 cup

A very simple lasagna, this recipe saves the step of precooking the noodles. Ensure that lasagna noodles are completely covered, to allow them to soften while standing.

*Recipe has been developed for use with 19 oz or 28 oz can sizes. Nutritional analysis based on 19 oz size only.

Brown meat in large nonstick skillet; drain off fat. Stir in tomatoes, breaking apart with fork; add basil and thyme. Bring to boil; reduce heat and simmer 5 minutes.

In food processor or blender, process cottage cheese until almost smooth. Add green onions and oregano; blend well.

Spoon half of tomato mixture evenly into bottom of 3.5 L (13 x 9 inch) baking pan. Top with 3 noodles, half the cottage cheese mixture and half the mozzarella cheese. Repeat layers.
Top with 3 noodles; spread remaining tomato mixture evenly over noodles. Sprinkle with Parmesan cheese. Cover and chill several hours or overnight.

Bake, uncovered, in 180°C (350°F) oven for about 50 minutes or until bubbling and noodles are tender. Let stand 10 minutes before serving.

Makes 8 servings, each 224 g/8 oz.

FOOD CHOICE VALUE *per serving*

Each Serving: 1/8 of recipe

4	☑ *Protein Choices*
1	☐ *Starchy Choice*
1	◪ *Fruits & Vegetables Choice*

24 g	Carbohydrate
30 g	Protein
12 g	Total Fat
1373	kilojoules (327 Calories)

CAKES
COOKIES & DESSERTS

	Protein	Starchy	Milk	Fruits & Vegetables	Fats & Oils	Page
Table of Equivalent Sweetness for Sugar Substitutes						216
Chocolate Truffles				1	1	217
Fruit Trifle		1	1/2	1		217
Chocolate Sauce					1/2	218
Yogurt Cream Frosting					1	218
Banana Cake		1		1	1	219
Carrot Cake		1/2		1	1/2	220
Pumpkin Chiffon Pie	1/2	1		1/2	1 1/2	221
Blueberry Lemon Cheesecake	1			2	1	222
Low-Cal Raspberry Cheesecake	1 1/2	1		1/2		223
Tangerine Cheesecake	1/2	1/2		1	2	224
Blender Cherry Mousse	1/2			1 1/2		225
Banana Cream Pie		1		1	1 1/2	226
Lemon Cream Pie	1/2	1		1/2	1 1/2	227
Peach Soufflé				1		228
Apricot Softie (Photo: p. 231)	1/2			1/2		229
Almond Crescent Cookies *(Photo: p. 231)*		1			1 1/2	230
Strawberry and Raspberry Bavarois (Photo: p. 232)	1/2			1		233
Coffee Soufflé (Photo: p. 232)	1			1/2	3	234
Cocoa Cream Pie	1/2	1		1/2	2	235
Cream Cheese and Strawberry Crepes	1			1		236
Fruit and Lemon Mousse				1	1	237
Fruit Shortcakes		1			1	238
Chocolate Fruit Mousse				1/2	1/2	239
Layered Fruit Pudding			1/2	1 1/2		240
Orange Bavarian				1	1/2	241
Light Bavarian Tarts				1		242

The Food Choice Values on each recipe do not include accompanying foods which are suggested in many of the recipes and shown in some of the photographs.

Table of Equivalent Sweetness for Sugar Substitute

SUGAR	SUGAR SUBSTITUTE
10 mL/2 tsp ....(32 Calories)	1 packet* ....(4 Calories)
40 mL/8 tsp................(128 Calories)	4 packets ....(16 Calories)
50 mL/1/4 cup ....(192 Calories)	6 packets ....(24 Calories)
75 mL/1/3 cup ....(253 Calories)	8 packets ....(32 Calories)
125 mL/1/2 cup ....(384 Calories)	12 packets ....(48 Calories)
150 mL/2/3 cup ....(507 Calories)	16 packets................(64Calories)
250 mL/1 cup ....(768 Calories)	24 packets ....(96 Calories)

1 Calorie = 4.2 kilojoules

Notes:

1. *Refers to Retail food/drug store sold packets, where 1 packet = 2 tsp of sugar sweetness. Don't confuse this with some Restaurant packets, where 1 packet = 1 tsp sugar sweetness. Check the package information.

2. Spoon-for-Spoon "Bulk" form of Sugar substitute is the same sweetness as sugar, ie. 1 tsp = 1 tsp. This form is more convenient for large measures. The Spoon-for-Spoon, Bulk format was used for all recipe nutritional analysis.

3. Most Liquid forms of Sugar substitutes are sweeter than dry granule forms; with 1/2 tsp = 2 tsp sugar sweetness. This may vary between brands. Check the package.

4. When Measuring; choose either Metric or Imperial measures throughout the whole recipe. Don't switch back and forth. Metric and Imperial measures are sometimes rounded for ease of measuring; as below:

    15 mL = 1 tbsp, but 25 mL is measured as 2 tbsp
    1 tbsp = 3 tsp, 4 tbsp = 1/4 cup = 50mL

Chocolate Truffles

Here's the perfect easy answer to any sweet tooth.

30 g	unsweetened chocolate	1 oz
20 mL	low-fat cream cheese	4 tsp
50 mL	graham cracker crumbs	1/4 cup
	Sugar substitute equivalent to 20 mL (4 tsp) sugar	
15 mL	ground almonds	1 tbsp

Melt chocolate in small bowl over pan of hot water; remove from heat. Beat in cream cheese. Add graham cracker crumbs and sweetener; mix well.

Refrigerate until chilled. Form into nine small balls. Roll in ground almonds to coat. Store in cool place. Serve at room temperature.

Makes 9 truffles.

Fruit Trifle

Here's a light and simple variation of a timeless dessert. For special occasions, use the prettiest glass serving dishes you can find.

500 mL	cubed angel food cake	2 cups
250 mL	fresh fruit	1 cup
2	containers (175 g each) low fat artificially sweetened strawberry yogurt	2

In 4 glass parfait glasses or other serving dishes, layer half of cake, fruit and yogurt; repeat layers.

Makes 4 servings.

See "Table of Equivalent Sweetness for Sugar Substitutes" at beginning of this recipe section.

FOOD CHOICE VALUE *per serving*

Each Serving: 2 Truffles
1 Fruits & Vegetables Choice
1 Fats & Oils Choice

6 g Carbohydrate
2 g Protein
6 g Total Fat
336 kilojoules (80 Calories)

FOOD CHOICE VALUE *per serving*

Each Serving: 1/4 of recipe
1 Starchy Choice
1/2 Milk Choice (skim)
1 Fruits & Vegetables Choice

26 g Carbohydrate
5 g Protein
0 g Total Fat
521 kilojoules (124 Calories)

Chocolate Sauce

Serve hot or cold over your favorite frozen yogurt or ice cream.
This sauce can be kept refrigerated about 2 weeks

150 mL	*evaporated skim milk*	*2/3 cup*
90 g	*unsweetened chocolate*	*3 oz.*
15 mL	*cornstarch*	*1 tbsp*
15 mL	*apple juice or water*	*1 tbsp*

Sugar substitute equivalent to 250 mL (1 cup) sugar*

In heavy saucepan, combine milk and chocolate; cook over very
low heat until chocolate melts, whisking occasionally.

Combine cornstarch and juice; whisk into chocolate mixture.
Cook over low heat until thickened, about 10 minutes, whisking
occasionally. Remove from heat; stir in sweetener.

Makes 250 mL (1 cup) or 8 servings, 30 mL/2 tbsp each.

For an even easier sauce, use premelted unsweetened chocolate.

Yogurt Cream Frosting

This is great for banana cake, carrot cake, lemon cake or spice cake!

1	*pkg (250 g/1/2 lb) light cream cheese, softened*	*1*
125 mL	*plain low-fat yogurt*	*1/2 cup*
	Sugar substitute equivalent to 125 mL (1/2 cup) sugar*	
5 mL	*dried lemon rind*	*1 tsp*
5 mL	*vanilla*	*1 tsp*

In bowl, blend cream cheese and yogurt until smooth. Stir in
sweetener, lemon rind and vanilla. Refrigerate until chilled.

Makes 500 mL (2 cups) or 16 servings, 30 mL/2 tbsp each.

KID'S FAVORITE

FOOD CHOICE VALUE *per serving*

Each Serving: 30 mL/2 tbsp

1/2 ▲ *Fats & Oils Choice*

3 g	*Carbohydrate*
1 g	*Protein*
2 g	*Total Fat*
118	*kilojoules (28 Calories)*

**See "Table of Equivalent
Sweetness for Sugar Substitutes"
at beginning of this recipe section.*

FOOD CHOICE VALUE *per serving*

Each Serving: 30 mL/2 tbsp

1 ▲ *Fats & Oils Choice*

2 g	*Carbohydrate*
2 g	*Protein*
4 g	*Total Fat*
197	*kilojoules (47 Calories)*

Banana Cake

If desired, you can frost the cooled cake between layers and on top with Yogurt Cream Frosting (see previous page).

See "Table of Equivalent Sweetness for Sugar Substitutes" at beginning of this recipe section.

500 mL	*all-purpose flour*	*2 cups*
15 mL	*baking powder*	*1 tbsp*
2 mL	*salt*	*1/2 tsp*
50 mL	*vegetable oil*	*1/4 cup*
2	*eggs*	*2*
125 mL	*skim milk*	*1/2 cup*
5 mL	*vanilla*	*1 tsp*
250 mL	*mashed ripe bananas*	*1 cup*

GLAZE

1 mL	*cinnamon*	*1/4 tsp*
	*Sugar substitute equivalent to 125 mL (1/2 cup) sugar	
50 mL	*boiling water*	*3 tbsp*

In bowl, sift together flour, baking powder and salt. In separate bowl, blend oil, eggs, skim milk and vanilla until smooth; stir in bananas. Add to dry ingredients and stir just until moistened. Pour evenly into two 1.2 L (8 inch) round cake pans sprayed with nonstick coating. Bake in 180°C (350°F) oven 20 minutes or until cake tester inserted near centre comes out clean.

Glaze: Combine cinnamon, sweetener and boiling water. Using fork, prick holes approximately 2.5 cm (1 inch) apart on top of each layer. Drizzle glaze evenly over each layer. Let cool in pans 10 minutes. Remove from pans; let cool completely on racks.

Makes 12 servings.

FOOD CHOICE VALUE *per serving*

Each Serving: 1/12 of recipe

1	□	*Starchy Choice*
1	◨	*Fruits & Vegetables Choice*
1	◣	*Fats & Oils Choice*

23 g	*Carbohydrate*
4 g	*Protein*
5 g	*Total Fat*
647	*kilojoules (154 Calories)*

Carrot Cake

Try it alone or with Yogurt Cream frosting recipe (page 218).

8	egg whites	8
125 mL	packed brown sugar	1/2 cup
125 mL	vegetable oil	1/2 cup
125 mL	plain low-fat yogurt	1/2 cup
250 mL	all-purpose flour	1 cup
250 mL	whole wheat flour	1 cup
10 mL	baking powder	2 tsp
2 mL	baking soda	1/2 tsp
2 mL	salt	1/2 tsp
10 mL	cinnamon	2 tsp
5 mL	ginger	1 tsp
2 mL	nutmeg	1/2 tsp
750 mL	grated raw carrots	3 cups
250 mL	drained crushed pineapple	1 cup
250 mL	raisins	1 cup

In large bowl, beat egg whites until foamy; beat in sugar until light. Beat in oil and yogurt; mix thoroughly.

Add flours, baking powder, baking soda, salt, cinnamon, ginger and nutmeg; stir until combined. Stir in carrots, pineapple, raisins.

Pour into greased and floured 3.5 L (13 x 9 inch) rectangular pan. Bake in 180°C (350°F) oven for 40 to 50 minutes or until tester inserted in centre comes out clean.

Makes 36 thin slices.

FOOD CHOICE VALUE *per serving*

Each Serving: 1 slice (1/36 of recipe)

1/2 ☐ *Starchy Choice*

1 ◩ *Fruits & Vegetables Choice*

1/2 ▲ *Fats & Oils Choice*

15 g	Carbohydrate
2 g	Protein
3 g	Total Fat
391	kilojoules (93 Calories)

Pumpkin Chiffon Pie

Luscious yet light, this pie is a perfect way to end a harvest-time meal.

See "Table of Equivalent Sweetness for Sugar Substitutes" at beginning of this recipe section.

CRUST

250 mL	all-purpose flour	1 cup
50 mL	diet margarine	1/4 cup
45 mL	cold water	3 tbsp

PUMPKIN FILLING

1	envelope unflavored gelatin	1
250 mL	skim milk	1 cup
2	eggs, separated	2
5 mL	cornstarch	1 tsp
15 mL	diet margarine	1 tbsp
5 mL	vanilla	1 tsp
500 mL	canned unseasoned pumpkin purée	2 cups
	Sugar substitute equivalent to 125 mL (1/2 cup) sugar	
5 mL	pumpkin pie spice	1 tsp
1	packet low-calorie whipped topping mix	1

Crust: In food processor, combine flour and margarine; process with on-off motion, until in coarse crumbs. Add water and blend until mixture forms a ball. Roll out on floured surface to 30 cm (12 inch) circle; line 23 cm (9 inch) pie plate. Trim edges. Cover pastry with 23 cm (9 inch) circle of waxed paper; prick holes through paper and pastry with fork. Weight down with uncooked dried beans or rice; bake in 180°C (350°F) oven 10 minutes. Remove beans and paper; bake 15 to 20 minutes or until lightly browned. Let cool.

Filling: Combine gelatin and 50 mL (1/4 cup) milk; let soften 5 minutes. In saucepan, blend egg yolks, 50 mL (1/4 cup) milk and cornstarch; cook over low heat until thickened. Stir in gelatin mixture. Add margarine; stir to blend. Remove from heat. Stir in vanilla, pumpkin purée, sweetener and pumpkin pie spice. Let cool.

Beat egg whites until stiff, but not dry, peaks form; set aside. Prepare whipped topping according to package directions, substituting 125 mL (1/2 cup) milk for water. Fold egg whites and half of whipped topping into pumpkin mixture. Pour into crust and spread evenly. Garnish with remaining whipped topping.

Makes 8 servings.

FOOD CHOICE VALUE *per serving*

Each Serving: 1/8 of recipe

1/2	☑ Protein Choice
1	☐ Starchy Choice
1/2	◪ Fruits & Vegetables Choice
1 1/2	▲ Fats & Oils Choices

22 g	Carbohydrate
6 g	Protein
8 g	Total Fat
764	kilojoules (182 Calories)

Blueberry Lemon Cheesecake

For a delicious flavor alternative, you can substitute raspberry spread, syrup and berries for the blueberries.

50 mL	toasted wheat germ	3 tbsp
750 mL	part-skim ricotta cheese, drained	3 cups
3	eggs	3
	Sugar substitute equivalent to 150 mL (2/3 cup) sugar.*	
75 mL	plain low-fat yogurt	1/3 cup
125 mL	cornstarch	1/2 cup
5 mL	baking powder	1 tsp
25 mL	butter or soft margarine, melted	2 tbsp
10 mL	grated lemon rind	2 tsp
5 mL	vanilla	1 tsp
125 mL	no-sugar-added blueberry spread	1/2 cup
36	fresh blueberries	36
250 mL	no-sugar-added spreadable blueberry syrup	1 cup

Grease bottom and 2.5 cm (1 inch) up sides of 2.5 L (9 inch) springform pan. Add wheat germ and tilt pan until bottom and sides are coated.

In large bowl, beat together ricotta cheese, eggs, sugar and yogurt until smooth. Combine cornstarch and baking powder; blend into cheese mixture. Add butter, lemon rind and vanilla; stir until well combined.

Spread half the batter in prepared pan. Beat blueberry spread lightly; spread over batter. Top with remaining half of batter. Bake in 160°C (325°F) oven 55 to 60 minutes or until set. Cool then chill. Slice and garnish each serving with 3 fresh blueberries and 20 mL (4 tsp) blueberry syrup.

Makes 12 servings.

See "Table of Equivalent Sweetness for Sugar Substitutes" at beginning of this recipe section.

FOOD CHOICE VALUE	per serving

Each Serving: 1/12 of recipe

1	☑ *Protein Choice*
2	☐ *Fruits & Vegetables Choices*
1	▲ *Fats & Oils Choice*

20 g	Carbohydrate
10 g	Protein
8 g	Total Fat
836	kilojoules (199 Calories)

Low-Cal Raspberry Cheesecake

No one will guess that this luscious dessert is so low in calories and fat. For a lovely presentation, top with fresh berries.

250 mL	*graham wafer crumbs*	*1 cup*
175 mL	*plain low-fat yogurt*	*3/4 cup*
500 mL	*low-fat cottage cheese*	*2 cups*
50 mL	*no-sugar-raspberry spread*	*1/4 cup*
1	*package (11 g) artificially sweetened raspberry jelly powder*	*1*
125 mL	*boiling water*	*1/2 cup*
2	*egg whites*	*2*
	Fresh seasonal fruit (optional)	

In small bowl, combine graham wafer crumbs and 45 mL (3 tbsp) yogurt. Press onto bottom of 2 L (8 inch) springform pan. Bake in 190°C (375°F) oven 8 to 10 minutes. Cool thoroughly; chill.

Meanwhile, in blender or food processor, blend cottage cheese until smooth. Transfer to bowl; stir in remaining yogurt and raspberry spread.

In small bowl, combine jelly powder and boiling water; stir until completely dissolved. Stir into cheese mixture.

In bowl, beat egg whites until soft peaks form; fold into cheese mixture. Pour into prepared crust. Chill 3 hours or overnight. Before serving, garnish with fresh fruit, if desired.

Makes 8 servings.

FOOD CHOICE VALUE *per serving*

Each Serving: 1/8 of recipe

1 1/2 ☑ *Protein Choices*

1 ☐ *Starchy Choice*

1/2 ◧ *Fruits & Vegetables Choice*

---

19 g   *Carbohydrate*

12 g   *Protein*

2 g   *Total Fat*

592   *kilojoules (141 Calories)*

Tangerine Cheesecake

An interesting double-layer effect is created by pressing the crust only half-way up the sides of the pan and then completely filling the pan with the cheese mixture.

See "Table of Equivalent Sweetness for Sugar Substitutes" at beginning of this recipe section.

CRUST

500 mL	graham cracker crumbs	2 cups
125 mL	diet margarine, melted	1/2 cup

TANGERINE FILLING

375 g	low-calorie cream cheese	3/4 lb
250 mL	part-skim ricotta cheese	1 cup
	Sugar substitute equivalent to 75 mL (1/3 cup) sugar*	
1	envelope unflavored gelatin	1
250 mL	orange juice	1 cup
1	packet low-calorie whipped topping mix	1
125 mL	skim milk	1/2 cup
250 mL	peeled, seeded and chopped tangerines (about 2)	1 cup
1	tangerine, peeled and sectioned	1

Crust: Blend cracker crumbs and margarine; press over bottom and halfway up sides of 2.5 L (9 inch) springform pan sprayed with nonstick vegetable spray. Bake in 180°C (350°F) oven 10 minutes. Let cool.

Filling: In bowl, blend together cream cheese and ricotta cheese; add sweetener. In small saucepan, sprinkle gelatin over tangerine juice; let soften 1 minute. Heat, stirring constantly, until gelatin dissolves, about 3 minutes. Add to cheese mixture; blend until smooth.

Prepare whipped topping according to package directions, substituting milk for water; fold into cheese mixture. Stir in chopped tangerine. Spoon into crust and spread evenly. Chill 4 to 6 hours. Garnish with tangerine sections.

Makes 16 servings.

FOOD CHOICE VALUE	per serving
Each Serving: 1/16 of recipe	
1/2 ☑ *Protein Choice*	
1/2 ☐ *Starchy Choice*	
1 ◪ *Fruits & Vegetables Choice*	
2 ▲ *Fats & Oils Choices*	
17 g	Carbohydrate
6 g	Protein
11 g	Total Fat
785	kilojoules (187 Calories)

Blender Cherry Mousse

This elegant dessert is simple to prepare. Just remember to allow mousse to chill for 4 to 6 hours.

See "Table of Equivalent Sweetness for Sugar Substitutes" at beginning of this recipe section.

1	egg	1
2	envelopes unflavored gelatin	2
15 mL	cornstarch	1 tbsp
150 mL	cranberry juice (sweetened)	2/3 cup
15 mL	cold water	1 tbsp
250 mL	boiling water	1 cup
500 mL	fresh Bing cherries, pitted	2 cups
250 mL	plain low-fat yogurt	1 cup

*Sugar substitute equivalent to 75 mL (1/3 cup) sugar

In bowl, combine egg, gelatin, cornstarch, cranberry juice and cold water; stir to blend. Add boiling water; blend thoroughly.

In food processor or blender, purée cherries; add gelatin mixture, yogurt and sweetener and blend until smooth. Chill 4 to 6 hours or until set. Blend again before serving in dessert dishes.

Makes 8 servings, 125 mL (1/2 cup) each.

FOOD CHOICE VALUE *per serving*

Each Serving: 1/8 of recipe

1/2 ☑ *Protein Choice*

1 1/2 ◪ *Fruits & Vegetables Choices*

---

14 g	Carbohydrate
5 g	Protein
1 g	Total Fat
336	kilojoules *(80 Calories)*

Banana Cream Pie

Here's a dessert that will appeal to both young and old.

CRUST

500 mL	*graham cracker crumbs*	*2 cups*
125 mL	*diet margarine, melted*	*1/2 cup*

BANANA FILLING

1	*envelope unflavored gelatin*	*1*
250 mL	*skim milk*	*1 cup*
175 mL	*part-skim ricotta cheese*	*3/4 cup*
10 mL	*vanilla*	*2 tsp*
3	*medium fresh bananas, peeled and sliced*	*3*

Sugar substitute equivalent to 50 mL (1/4 cup) sugar*

TOPPING

2	*egg whites*	*2*

Sugar Substitute equivalent to 50 mL (1/4 cup) sugar

Nutmeg

*See "Table of Equivalent Sweetness for Sugar Substitutes" at beginning of this recipe section.

Crust: Blend cracker crumbs with margarine; press over bottom and sides of 20 cm (8 inch) pie plate. Bake in 180°C (350°F) oven 8 to 10 minutes. Let cool.

Filling: In small saucepan, sprinkle gelatin over 125 mL (1/2 cup) milk; let soften 5 minutes. Heat, stirring constantly, until gelatin dissolves, about 3 minutes.

In food processor or blender, blend ricotta cheese until smooth; add gelatin mixture, remaining 125 mL (1/2 cup) milk and vanilla. Blend until smooth. Reserve 250 mL (1 cup) mixture.

Add sweetener and 2 bananas to remaining mixture in food processor; blend until smooth. Place remaining banana slices on bottom of pie crust. Pour banana cream mixture over top. Chill 1 hour.

Topping: In bowl, beat egg whites until foamy; gradually add sweetener and continue beating until stiff peaks form. Fold into reserved ricotta cheese mixture. Spoon over chilled banana cream. Chill 4 to 6 hours until set. Sprinkle with nutmeg.

Makes 12 servings.

FOOD CHOICE VALUE *per serving*

Each Serving: 1/12 of recipe

1	☐	*Starchy Choice*
1	◩	*Fruits & Vegetables Choice*
1 1/2	◣	*Fats & Oils Choices*

23 g	*Carbohydrate*
5 g	*Protein*
7 g	*Total Fat*
728	*kilojoules (173 Calories)*

Lemon Cream Pie

Use uncooked, dried beans or rice to weight down pastry crust to avoid air bubbles while baking.

See "Table of Equivalent Sweetness for Sugar Substitutes" at beginning of this recipe section.

CRUST

250 mL	all-purpose flour	1 cup
50 mL	diet margarine	1/4 cup
45 mL	cold water	3 tbsp

LEMON CUSTARD

3	egg yolks	3
15 mL	cornstarch	1 tbsp
1	envelope unflavored gelatin	1
175 mL	lemon juice	3/4 cup
175 mL	boiling water	3/4 cup
15 mL	grated lemon rind	1 tbsp
15 mL	diet margarine	1 tbsp

Sugar substitute equivalent to 125 mL (1/2 cup) sugar

TOPPING

2	egg whites	2
1	packet low-calorie whipped topping mix	1
125 mL	skim milk	1/2 cup
1	lemon, thinly sliced	1

Crust: In food processor, combine flour and margarine; process with on-off motion until in coarse crumbs. Add water and blend until mixture forms a ball. Roll out on floured surface to 30 cm (12 inch) circle, line 23 cm (9 inch) pie plate. Trim edges. Cover pastry with 23 cm (9 inch) circle of waxed paper; prick holes through paper and pastry with fork. Weight down with dried beans or rice; bake in 180°C (350°F) oven 10 minutes. Remove beans and paper; bake 15 to 20 minutes or until lightly browned. Let cool.

Custard: In food processor or blender, blend egg yolks, cornstarch, gelatin and lemon juice; add boiling water and blend thoroughly. Blend in lemon rind and margarine. Pour into small pan and heat to boiling, stirring constantly, until thickened. Let cool slightly; stir in sweetener. Pour into pie crust. Chill for 2 hours.

Topping: In bowl, beat egg whites until stiff, but not dry, peaks form. Prepare whipped topping according to package directions, substituting milk for water. Gently fold in egg whites. Spread over chilled custard. Garnish with lemon slices. Serve immediately.

Makes 8 servings.

FOOD CHOICE VALUE *per serving*

Each Serving: 1/8 of recipe

1/2	☑ Protein Choice
1	☐ Starchy Choice
1/2	◨ Fruits & Vegetables Choice
1 1/2	◣ Fats & Oils Choices

19 g	Carbohydrate
5 g	Protein
8 g	Total Fat
722	kilojoules (172 Calories)

Peach Soufflé

Soufflés are easy to prepare. Just remember to serve them straight from the oven. Serve this plain or with a fruit sauce.

6	*egg whites*	6
1 mL	*cream of tartar*	1/4 tsp
Pinch	*salt*	Pinch
25 mL	*cornstarch*	2 tbsp
500 mL	*sliced peeled fresh peaches*	2 cups
10 mL	*almond extract*	2 tsp

Sugar substitute equivalent to 50 mL (1/4 cup) sugar*

*See "Table of Equivalent Sweetness for Sugar Substitutes" at beginning of this recipe section.

Beat egg whites with cream of tartar and salt until stiff, but not dry, peaks form. Whip in cornstarch.

In food processor or blender, purée peaches; transfer to bowl and add almond extract. Gently fold in egg whites.

Pour into 2 L (8 cup) soufflé dish sprayed with nonstick vegetable spray. Bake in 220°C (425°F) oven 10 minutes. Reduce heat to 190°C (375°F); bake 20 minutes. Remove from oven; sprinkle with sweetener.

Makes 8 servings, 250 mL (1 cup) each.

FOOD CHOICE VALUE *per serving*

Each Serving: 1/8 of recipe

1 ◼ *Fruits & Vegetables Choice*

8 g	*Carbohydrate*
3 g	*Protein*
0 g	*Total Fat*
181	*kilojoules (43 Calories)*

Apricot Softie

PHOTO ON PAGE 231

You can use either fresh apricots (skinned), or canned apricots in juice , drained. Don't use dried apricots, as they contain a lot of sugar.

†*See "Table of Equivalent Sweetness for Sugar Substitutes" at beginning of this recipe section.*

Enjoy this fresh-tasting, easy-to-make dessert without any pangs of guilt – it's healthy and low-calorie.

375 mL	apricots*	1 1/2 cups
250 mL	plain low-fat yogurt	1 cup
2	egg whites	2

†Sugar substitute equivalent to
30 mL (2tbsp) sugar
Apricot slices (optional)

In food processor or blender, purée apricots; add yogurt and process for 30 seconds or until combined.

In medium bowl, beat egg whites until stiff peaks form; fold in low-calorie sweetener. Carefully fold apricot mixture into egg whites.

Spoon into 6 parfait glasses or serving dishes. Cover and refrigerate until set, about 30 minutes.

Just before serving, garnish with apricot slices, if desired.

Makes 6 servings.

FOOD CHOICE VALUE *per serving*

Each Serving: 1/6 of recipe

1/2 ▨ *Protein Choice*

1/2 ◪ *Fruits & Vegetables Choice*

8 g	Carbohydrate
4 g	Protein
0 g	Total Fat
214	kilojoules (51 Calories)

Almond Crescent Cookies

Here's a festive cookie that shouldn't be reserved for just the
Yuletide season.

PHOTO ON PAGE 231.

300 mL	*butter, softened*	*1 1/4 cups*
250 mL	*icing sugar*	*1 cup*
10 mL	*vanilla*	*2 tsp*
550 mL	*all-purpose flour*	*2 1/4 cups*
2 mL	*salt*	*1/2 tsp*
250 mL	*ground almonds*	*1 cup*

In bowl, cream butter; beat in sugar and vanilla. Stir together flour
and salt; gradually add to creamed mixture in parts. Stir in almonds.

Form into 2.5 cm (1 inch) balls; shape into crescents. Place on
ungreased baking sheets and bake in 160°C (325°F) oven for 12
to 15 minutes or until lightly golden.

Makes about 6 dozen, each cookie 28 g/1 oz.

FOOD CHOICE VALUE *per serving*

Each Serving: 2 cookies

1	☐	*Starchy Choice*
1 1/2	▲	*Fats & Oils Choices*

10 g	*Carbohydrate*
2 g	*Protein*
8 g	*Total Fat*
512	*kilojoules (122 Calories)*

Almond Crescent Cookies (p.230)

Apricot Softie (p.229)

Coffee Soufflé (p.234)

Strawberry and Raspberry Bavarois (p.233)

Strawberry and Raspberry Bavarois

PHOTO ON PAGE 232

Prepare this in a ring mould, then at serving time fill the centre with fresh berries.

See "Table of Equivalent Sweetness for Sugar Substitutes" at beginning of this recipe section.

2	egg yolks	2
250 mL	skim milk	1 cup
1	envelope unflavored gelatin	1
50 mL	cold water	1/4 cup
25 mL	plain low-fat yogurt	2 tbsp
5 mL	vanilla	1 tsp
	*Sugar substitute equivalent to 50 mL (1/4 cup) sugar	
250 mL	fresh or frozen mixed strawberries and raspberries, lightly crushed	1 cup

SAUCE

250 mL	fresh or frozen strawberries or raspberries	1 cup
	Sugar substitute equivalent to 20 mL (4 tsp) sugar	

In saucepan, combine egg yolks with milk; cook over low heat until mixture just coats back of spoon. Remove from heat; transfer to bowl and let cool.

In small saucepan, soften gelatin in cold water; heat, stirring, over low heat until dissolved. Let cool.

Add gelatin to bowl; stir in yogurt, vanilla and sweetener. Fold in fruit. Pour into 1 L (4 cup) ring mould. Refrigerate at least 4 hours or until set.

Sauce: Purée fruit and sweeten to taste with sweetener. Invert bavarois onto chilled serving platter; pour purée around base.

Makes 6 servings.

FOOD CHOICE VALUE *per serving*

Each Serving: 1/6 of recipe

1/2 ☑ *Protein Choice*

1 ☐ *Fruits & Vegetables Choice*

10 g	Carbohydrate
4 g	Protein
2 g	Total Fat
311	kilojoules *(74 Calories)*

Coffee Soufflé

For an attractive presentation, garnish this dessert with coffee beans
and whipped cream rosettes.

500 mL	*skim milk*	*2 cups*
4	*eggs, separated*	*4*
2	*envelopes unflavored gelatin*	*2*
50 mL	*cold water*	*1/4 cup*
15 mL	*instant coffee granules*	*1 tbsp*
	Sugar substitute equivalent to 50 mL (1/4 cup) sugar*	
500 mL	*whipping cream, lightly whipped*	*2 cups*

In saucepan, bring milk just to boil; slowly add beaten egg yolks,
whisking well. Cook, stirring occasionally, until mixture thickens
and coats back of spoon. Do not boil. Transfer to bowl and let cool.

In separate saucepan, soften gelatin in cold water; stir over low
heat until dissolved. Add to bowl along with coffee granules and
sweetener. Gently fold in whipped cream. Beat egg whites until
stiff; fold into mixture.

Make paper collar by folding waxed paper in half and fitting around
outside of 1.5 L (6 cup) soufflé dish at least 10 cm (4 inches) above
top of dish. Secure with tape. Carefully spoon soufflé into dish. Chill
at least 3 hours. Remove paper collar.

Makes 10 servings.

PHOTO ON PAGE 232

**See "Table of Equivalent
Sweetness for Sugar Substitutes" at
beginning of this recipe section.*

FOOD CHOICE VALUE *per serving*

Each Serving: 1/10 of recipe

1	☑ *Protein Choice*
1/2	◨ *Fruits & Vegetables Choice*
3	▲ *Fats & Oils Choices*

5 g	*Carbohydrate*
6 g	*Protein*
18 g	*Total Fat*
874	*kilojoules (208 Calories)*

Cocoa Cream Pie

Garnish this elegant dessert with a dusting of cocoa.

See "Table of Equivalent Sweetness for Sugar Substitutes" at beginning of this recipe section.

GRAHAM CRACKER CRUST

75 mL	diet margarine	1/3 cup
300 mL	graham cracker crumbs	1 1/4 cups

FILLING

1	envelope unflavored gelatin	1
375 mL	skim milk	1 1/2 cups
175 mL	part-skim ricotta cheese	3/4 cup
15 mL	vanilla	1 tbsp
*Sugar substitute equivalent to 125 mL (1/2 cup) sugar		
50 mL	cocoa	1/4 cup
1	packet low-calorie whipped topping mix	1

Graham Cracker Crust: In bowl, cut margarine into crumbs until mixture resembles coarse crumbs. Press firmly onto bottom and side of 20 or 23 cm (8 or 9 inch) pie plate. Bake in 180°C (350°F) oven 8 to 10 minutes. Cool.

Filling: In small saucepan, sprinkle gelatin over 125 mL (1/2 cup) skim milk; let stand 1 minute. Heat, stirring constantly, until gelatin dissolves.

In blender or food processor, blend ricotta until smooth; blend in gelatin mixture, remaining milk and vanilla until completely smooth. Remove half to bowl and chill for 30 minutes.

To mixture in blender, add half of sweetener and cocoa; blend thoroughly. Pour into crust; chill for 30 minutes or until partially set.

Prepare whipped topping according to package directions, gradually adding remaining sweetener. Whisk into chilled mixture in bowl until blended. Spoon over chocolate layer; chill until set.

Makes 8 servings.

FOOD CHOICE VALUE *per serving*

Each Serving: 1/8 of recipe

1/2 ☑ *Protein Choice*
1 ☐ *Starchy Choice*
1/2 ◨ *Fruits & Vegetables Choice*
2 ▲ *Fats & Oils Choices*

20 g *Carbohydrate*
7 g *Protein*
12 g *Total Fat*
882 *kilojoules (210 Calories)*

Cream Cheese and Strawberry Crepes

Here's a special dessert you can assemble at the last minute if you make the crepes ahead of time.

CREPE

2	*eggs*	2
50 mL	*skim milk*	1/4 cup
25 mL	*water*	2 tbsp
50 mL	*all-purpose flour*	1/4 cup
0.5 mL	*salt*	1/8 tsp

FILLING

75 g	*light cream cheese, softened*	3 oz
90 mL	*dry curd cottage cheese*	6 tbsp

Sugar substitute equivalent to 50 mL (1/4 cup) sugar*

SAUCE

500 mL	*strawberries, coarsely chopped*	2 cups
15 mL	*lemon juice*	1 tbsp

Sugar substitute equivalent to 50 mL (1/4 cup) sugar

Crepe: In bowl, beat eggs, milk and water; beat in flour and salt just until smooth. Spray crepe pan with nonstick coating; heat over medium heat until hot. Spoon 25 mL (2 tbsp) batter into pan, rotating pan to spread evenly. Cook until edges of crepe are browned; turn crepe out onto plate. Repeat with remaining batter.

Filling: In blender, process cream cheese, cottage cheese and sweetener until smooth; set aside.

Sauce: Toss together strawberries, lemon juice and sweetener. When ready to serve, spoon 25 mL (2 tbsp) filling onto each crepe; roll up and place seamside down on plate. Serve with sauce.

Makes 6 servings, 2 crepes each.

*See "Table of Equivalent Sweetness for Sugar Substitutes" at beginning of this recipe section.

FOOD CHOICE VALUE *per serving*

Each Serving: 2 Crepes (1/6 recipe)

1	☑ *Protein Choice*
1	◨ *Fruits & Vegetables Choice*

10 g	*Carbohydrate*
6 g	*Protein*
4 g	*Total Fat*
454	*kilojoules (108 Calories)*

Fruit and Lemon Mousse

This tastes so rich you won't believe it's low in calories!

See "Table of Equivalent Sweetness for Sugar Substitutes" at beginning of this recipe section.

FRUIT

500 mL	*sliced fresh or frozen unsweetened strawberries*	*2 cups*

*Sugar substitute equivalent to 50 mL (1/4 cup) sugar

MOUSSE

1	*packet low-calorie whipped topping mix*	*1*
125 mL	*skim milk*	*1/2 cup*
25 mL	*lemon juice*	*2 tbsp*
15 mL	*grated lemon rind*	*1 tbsp*

Sugar substitute equivalent to 40 mL (8 tsp) sugar

CUSTARD

175 mL	*water*	*3/4 cup*
50 mL	*lemon juice*	*1/4 cup*
50 mL	*diet margarine*	*3 tbsp*
3	*eggs*	*3*
25 mL	*cornstarch*	*2 tbsp*

Sugar substitute equivalent to 150 mL (2/3 cup) sugar

Fruit: Sprinkle fruit with sweetener; toss gently and chill.

Mousse: Prepare whipped topping using the 125 mL(1/2 cup) milk according to package directions; fold in lemon juice and rind, and sweetener. Chill.

Custard: In small saucepan, mix water, lemon juice and margarine; heat to boiling. Beat eggs until creamy; add cornstarch and mix thoroughly. Stir a small amount of hot mixture into eggs. Whisk eggs into hot mixture; bring to boil, stirring constantly. Remove from heat; stir in sweetener. Chill.

When ready to serve, divide fruit among 8 dessert dishes. Spoon cold custard over fruit. Top with mousse. Garnish with lemon slices.

Makes 8 servings, 125 mL (1/2 cup) each.

FOOD CHOICE VALUE *per serving*

Each Serving: 1/8 of recipe

1 ◘ *Fruits & Vegetables Choice*

1 ▲ *Fats & Oils Choice*

10 g	*Carbohydrate*
3 g	*Protein*
5 g	*Total Fat*
395	*kilojoules (94 Calories)*

Fruit Shortcakes

Try this tender, flavorful alternative to calorie-packed traditional shortcakes.

325 mL	*all-purpose flour*	*1 1/3 cups*
125 mL	*whole wheat flour*	*1/2 cup*
15 mL	*baking powder*	*1 tbsp*
2 mL	*baking soda*	*1/2 tsp*
1 mL	*salt*	*1/4 tsp*
50 mL	*shortening*	*1/4 cup*
1	*container (175 g) plain low-fat yogurt*	*1*
1	*egg, lightly beaten*	*1*

In large bowl, combine flours, baking powder, baking soda and salt. Cut in shortening until well mixed. Combine yogurt and egg; add to dry mixture, stirring with fork to make soft, slightly sticky dough.

Gather into ball and knead gently on lightly floured surface about 8 times until smooth. Roll or pat out to 20 cm (8 inch) round about 2 cm (3/4 inch) thick.

Cut into 12 wedges. Bake on baking sheet in 200°C (400°F) oven 15 to 18 minutes or until golden brown. To serve, split in half while warm.

Makes 12 servings.

Add fresh or frozen berries sweetened without sugar, if desired. Be sure to count extra berries as part of your Fruit & Vegetables Choices.

FOOD CHOICE VALUE *per serving*

Each Serving: 1/12 of recipe

1	☐	*Starchy Choice*
1	▲	*Fats & Oils Choice*

16 g	*Carbohydrate*
3 g	*Protein*
4 g	*Total Fat*
487	*kilojoules (116 Calories)*

Chocolate Fruit Mousse

Spoon this rich-tasting, easy-to-make mousse over any combination of fruit. Try berries, sliced peaches, pears or apples for a fancy dessert that fits the season.

500 mL	*fresh strawberries, sweetened with sugar substitute*	*2 cups*
1	*pkg (30 g) white chocolate artificially sweetened dessert mousse mix*	*1*
1/2 oz	*unsweetened chocolate, melted*	*15 g*

Arrange fruit evenly among 6 stemmed glasses or other dessert dishes. Prepare mousse mix according to package directions; spoon evenly over fruit.

Drizzle melted chocolate on top of each dessert, swirling with knife to create attractive pattern. Chill.

Makes 6 servings.

FOOD CHOICE VALUE *per serving*

Each Serving: 1/6 of recipe

1/2 ◨ *Fruits & Vegetables Choice*

1/2 ◣ *Fats & Oils Choice*

7 g	*Carbohydrate*
1 g	*Protein*
3 g	*Total Fat*
218	*kilojoules (52 Calories)*

Layered Fruit Pudding

Dress up strawberries, cherries, plums, blackberries or other fresh seasonal fruit with this delicious creamy mixture.

1	*pkg (30g) artificially sweetened vanilla instant pudding*	*1*
500 mL	*skim milk*	*2 cups*
125 mL	*plain low-fat yogurt*	*1/2 cup*
500 mL	*halved strawberries*	*2 cups*
2	*peaches, peeled and cubed*	*2*
250 mL	*blueberries*	*1 cup*
500 mL	*seedless green grapes, halved*	*2 cups*
	Additional fruit or mint (optional)	

In medium bowl, prepare pudding mix with milk according to package directions; immediately fold in yogurt.

Meanwhile, layer strawberries, peaches, blueberries and grapes in glass serving bowl or 10 individual parfait glasses. Spoon pudding mixture over fruit. Cover and refrigerate several hours to blend flavors. Garnish with fruit or mint, if desired.

Makes 10 servings.

FOOD CHOICE VALUE *per serving*

Each Serving: 1/10 of recipe

1/2 ◆ *Milk Choice (skim)*

1 1/2 ◻ *Fruits & Vegetables Choices*

19 g	*Carbohydrate*
3 g	*Protein*
0 g	*Total Fat*
361	*kilojoules (86 Calories)*

Orange Bavarian

Lighter than a traditional Bavarian cream, this is a smooth and creamy treat.

See "Table of Equivalent Sweetness for Sugar Substitutes" at beginning of this recipe section.

2	*eggs, separated*	2
1	*envelope unflavored gelatin*	1
15 mL	*cornstarch*	1 tbsp
250 mL	*orange juice*	1 cup
15 mL	*grated orange rind*	1 tbsp
	*Sugar substitute equivalent to 75 mL (1/3 cup) sugar	
1	*packet low-calorie whipped topping mix*	1
125 mL	*skim milk*	1/2 cup
	Fresh orange slices	

In food processor or blender, blend egg yolks, gelatin, cornstarch and orange juice until smooth. Pour mixture into saucepan; bring to boil, stirring constantly. Reduce heat and simmer 5 minutes or until mixture thickens. Stir in orange rind. Let cool slightly. Stir in sweetener. Chill in refrigerator 15 minutes.

Prepare whipped topping according to package directions, substituting milk for water; set aside.

In separate bowl, beat egg whites until stiff, but not dry, peaks form. Gently fold egg whites and whipped topping into chilled orange mixture. Spoon into 1 L (4 cup) mold sprayed with nonstick vegetable spray. Chill several hours or overnight. Unmold and garnish with orange slices.

Makes 8 servings, 125 mL (1/2 cup) each.

FOOD CHOICE VALUE *per serving*

Each Serving: 1/8 of recipe

1 **☐ Fruits & Vegetables Choice**
1/2 **▲ Fats & Oils Choice**

9 g	Carbohydrate
3 g	Protein
2 g	Total Fat
160	kilojoules (63 Calories)

Light Bavarian Tarts

As eye-appealing as they are delicious, these sumptuous tarts are quick and easy to prepare and certain to win rave approval whenever you serve them. Guests won't believe that anything that looks so inviting can be so calorie-slim. Garnish with additional fruit, if desired.

2	*egg whites*	2
	Sugar substitute equivalent to	
	25 mL (2 tbsp) sugar*	
1 L	*crisp flake cereal, lightly crushed, (Eg.Corn Flakes)*	*4 cups*
175 mL	*cold skim milk*	*3/4 cup*
1	*pkg (30 g) chocolate or strawberry*	*1*
	artificially sweetened mousse mix	
250 mL	*strawberries, finely chopped*	*1cup*

*See "Table of Equivalent Sweetness for Sugar Substitute" at beginning of this recipe section.

In large bowl, beat egg whites with sweetener until soft peaks form. Fold in cereal until thoroughly coated. Drop mixture in twelve 5 cm (2 inch) mounds onto lightly greased baking sheet. With back of wet spoon, flatten each mound in centre, leaving edges slightly higher, to make 6 cm (2 1/2 inches) rounds. Bake in 200°C (400°F) oven 6 minutes. Cool.

Meanwhile, pour milk into deep bowl; add mousse mix. Beat on low speed with electric mixer until thickened, then whip at highest speed 3 to 5 minutes until fluffy.

Fold strawberries into mousse. Spoon mousse into tart shells, mounding and swirling each.

Makes 12 mini tarts.

FOOD CHOICE VALUE *per serving*

Each Serving: 1 tart

1	◨	*Fruits & Vegetables Choice*

10 g	*Carbohydrate*
2 g	*Protein*
1 g	*Total Fat*
227	*kilojoules (54 Calories)*